GEORGES BARRÈRE
and the Flute in America

An exhibit in the Music Division,
New York Public Library for the Performing Arts

November 12, 1994–February 4, 1995

Nancy Toff

The New York Flute Club, Inc.

1994

This catalog is dedicated to the memory of
Lewis J. Deveau (1925–1993),
employee of the Wm. S. Haynes Co., Inc. (1941–1993),
owner and president of the Wm. S. Haynes Co., Inc. (1976–1993),
and a longtime supporter of the New York Flute Club.

Published by the New York Flute Club, Inc. in commemoration of the
50th anniversary of the death of Georges Barrère and the 75th anniversary of the
New York Flute Club, which he founded.

Printed in U.S.A.

Design: Loraine Machlin
Catalog photography: Ira N. Toff
Editorial staff: Tara Deal, Patricia Harper, Paul McCarthy, Michael Ronall

This catalog has been printed with a generous grant from the Wm. S. Haynes Co., Inc.

NOTE: All spellings and punctuation in this catalog are faithful to the original documents
except for correction of obvious typographical errors. Throughout his career, Barrère was
inconsistent about the spelling of his given name; Georges and George were often used
interchangeably on his letterhead and programs.

On the cover: Pencil sketch of Georges Barrère at the New York Flute Club
by L.F. Grant, 1935 (catalog no. 129)

CONTENTS

PREFACE

This exhibit commemorates both the fiftieth anniversary of the death of Georges Barrère and the seventy-fifth anniversary season of the New York Flute Club, which he founded. In addition to the exhibit, the entire 1994–95 concert season of the New York Flute Club will recognize Barrère's contributions by programming works that were dedicated to him, that he premiered, and that he played regularly. It is an interesting and varied repertoire, as interesting and varied as his life.

Today, the New York Flute Club is the oldest organization of its kind in the country—one of some seventy-five, plus the National Flute Association, that provide educational and performance opportunities for flutists and composers for the flute. Thus we honor not only Barrère the man, but also the glorious, living tradition of French woodwind playing that he did so much to establish in America.

It is appropriate to note that many of the projects in which Barrère was involved continue today. He was fully cognizant of the challenges of running an organization to serve both amateur and professional flutists. In Barrère's day, members could play flute quartets with their president or accompanied works with the staff pianist; today members meet through a regular ensemble program. In Barrère's day, performances by his most gifted students were a fixture of the club's programs; today, we have a competition that showcases promising young players from many conservatories. From the club's earliest days, its concerts provided performance opportunities for leading professionals from New York and afar; today our concert series welcomes distinguished soloists from throughout the world.

Barrère made great efforts to program the works of his contemporaries, many of them also flutists; today the programs are equally likely to include works of contemporary flutist-composers. As a member of the New York Symphony, Barrère taught city high school students through the orchestra's scholarship program; today we continue this tradition through our community outreach program, which works with the Harlem School of the Arts and the La Guardia High School of the Performing Arts and Music and Art.

The New York Flute Club is proud of its distinguished past and of its longevity, but equally proud of its ability to maintain the ideals of its founder while adapting to changing needs. We hope that Georges Barrère would be pleased.

GEORGES BARRÈRE

1876–1944

"World's greatest virtuoso of the flute," "Monarch of flute players," "The Magic Flute Player"—all these appellations, bestowed by music critics, denote Georges Barrère's preeminent place in the history of American flute playing. The late-20th century observer will perhaps hear in these encomia pre-echoes of the publicity surrounding Jean-Pierre Rampal and James Galway since the 1960s, but, in fact, the flute renaissance for which they are responsible is a second renaissance: the first was Barrère's. As William Hullinger, then the leading flutist in Los Angeles, wrote in 1925, "Perhaps the foremost individual in rehabilitating the flute in America is Georges Barrère. By combining superb artistry with a discreet and dignified publicity and several transcontinental tours, he has easily taken the leadership; his decided departure from the pyrotechnical display long in vogue has done much to aid in an increased appreciation of the flute in its true musical setting."

Barrère's contribution was far broader and more significant than mere virtuosity, for he inspired major additions to the flute's solo and chamber repertoire. Though he did not believe in commissioning new works, he asked for them, inspired them, promoted them, and did everything but pay for them. As the most prominent early exemplar of the Paris Conservatoire woodwind tradition in the United States, he set a new standard for American woodwind performance. And he played a crucial role in the development of chamber music and the chamber symphony in his adopted country.

Purely as an individual accomplishment, Barrère's career was outstanding from the very beginning. A precocious virtuoso on the tin whistle, he was a sergeant in a schoolboy fife and drum corps until he entered the Paris Conservatoire at age fifteen. There he studied with Henri Altès and Paul Taffanel, winning the *premier prix* in 1895. He considered Taffanel the major influence on his musical career. Not only did Taffanel encourage the "classics"—notably Bach and Mozart—but he was responsible for commissioning some of the leading French composers to write competition pieces for the Conservatoire's annual examinations. Barrère followed this example both in his choice of repertoire and in his own collaborations with composers.

While still a student, Barrère was principal flute of the Société nationale, with which he played the premiere of Debussy's *Prélude à l'après-midi d'un faune* in 1894. He later held positions with the orchestras of the Geneva Exposition, Concerts Colonne, and Paris Opéra. An active private teacher, he was also a faculty member at Vincent D'Indy's Schola Cantorum—a likely influence on his interest in antiquarian repertoire.

In 1895 he founded the Société Moderne d'Instruments à Vent, essentially a revival of a similar group run by Taffanel from 1879 to 1893. Under Barrère's direction, the organization was responsible for inspiring and performing more than sixty new works by European composers. At the time Barrère came to musical maturity in France, opera was paramount. His artistic and financial success with the Société Moderne—in attracting composers to write for it, in securing funding from the French government, and in earning election to the French Academy—was extraordinary in such a milieu.

In 1905, when Walter Damrosch offered him the principal chair in the New York Symphony Orchestra, Barrère seized the opportunity to conquer a New World. He played in the Damrosch orchestra until it disbanded in 1928 and was clearly one of its star players. Barrère, recalled his colleague Winthrop Sargeant, was "our great aristocrat."

Always ambitious, Barrère made the most of his position in the orchestra. During his first year in New York, he organized the wind players into the New York Symphony Wind Instruments Club. In the summers, the New York Symphony traveled to various festivals, including, from 1920 to 1928, Chautauqua. There Barrère became a major presence. He began teaching at the Chautauqua summer school in 1921, and when the Chautauqua Symphony was founded after the demise of the New York Symphony, he became first flutist and assistant conductor, as well as regular conductor of the Chautauqua Little Symphony.

Barrère developed a solo career from his earliest days in New York. He was a frequent soloist with the New York Symphony, and despite early concessions to Damrosch's light programming for summer festivals, Barrère insisted on high-quality repertoire. He said of concerto appearances, "I always make up my programme so it compares favorably with that of any other soloist."

Having gained the attention of the critics and the public, Barrère soon began playing recitals, often with colleagues such as Arthur Whiting. Flute recitals were decidedly out of the ordinary in those days, but he did not stoop to his audiences, programming substantial works such as the Bach sonatas, the Schubert *Introduction and Variations*, and the Jarnach *Sonatine*. "Each time I play a solo," he wrote, "I make it a point to do something useful, either playing some good, very good, music to elevate the standard of our instrument or by playing some new worthy compositions which will help furnish an incentive for present day composers to write for our worthy instrument." The results were gratifying: As the *New York Sun* critic wrote in 1910, "During five years in New York, Mr. Barrère has won friends for that abused instrument, the flute; has shown that its repertory includes music of the masters instead of second class 'show pieces,' and that its players are really interpretative artists."

Barrère also earned the admiration of his colleagues. He was a fixture of New York musical circles: the Juilliard faculty, the Beethoven Association, the Bohemians (New York Musicians' Club), the Society for Publication of American Music, and many other organizations. In addition to his regular chamber music partners, he collaborated with the finest musicians of his day, including soprano Emma Calvé, violinist Albert Spalding, baritone David Bispham, the violin-and-piano duo of David and Clara Mannes, pianist Harold Bauer, and dancer Isadora Duncan. Duncan made gracious reference to her collaboration with Barrère in her autobiography: "There was a flutist who played so divinely the solo of the Happy Spirits in 'Orpheus' that I often found myself immobile on the stage with the tears flowing from my eyes, just from the ecstasy of listening to him."

Best known, perhaps, is Barrère's pivotal role in the universal adoption of the silver flute in the United States. At the time Barrère came to this country, the wooden flute predominated; the unique sound that he created with his Louis Lot silver instrument caused a near-revolution. French silver-flute players—notably Charles Molé and André Maquarre—had been in the Boston Symphony since 1887, but Carl Wehner continued to hold sway in New York with a wooden Boehm, and the leading flute maker, Wm. S. Haynes, made wooden instruments exclusively. Just thirteen years after Barrère's arrival, the Haynes Co.'s production had converted entirely to silver flutes, and Wehner's career had gone into rapid decline. In 1927 Barrère made news with his acquisition of a gold Haynes, and yet again in 1935 with his platinum flute—the first in the United States. Despite his own misgivings about those instruments, the race to precious metals was on.

As he had done in France, Barrère made enormous contributions to the entire woodwind section. He founded the Barrère Ensemble of Woodwind Instruments in 1910 and programmed American premieres of many works that had been written for the Société Moderne (Caplet's *Suite Persane* and Enesco's *Dixtuor,* for example). He also premiered numerous works by American composers. The concept of a permanent woodwind ensemble, in an era when the string quartet was the only form of chamber music to have any real prevalence, was daring but extremely well received. In 1931, Barrère founded the woodwind ensemble program at the Juilliard School. He used the ensemble sessions both to try out some of his own quintet arrangements and to train a new generation of superior woodwind players.

Throughout his American career, Barrère played in a wide variety of chamber groups. With cellist Paul Kéfer and pianist Lillie Sang-Collins he formed the Trio Rameau, devoted to French music. Beginning in 1909 he was involved in Arthur Whiting's Expositions of Classical and Modern Chamber Music, which presented innovative programs of baroque repertoire at East Coast universities. In 1913, Barrère, Kéfer, and harpist Carlos Salzedo formed the Trio de Lutèce, whose unusual repertoire included baroque sonatas and a number of arrangements by the multi-talented Salzedo, notably Debussy's *Children's Corner Suite* and Ravel's *Sonatine en trio.* In the 1930s Barrère was active with three other chamber groups: Barrère-Salzedo-Britt, a trio with Salzedo and cellist Horace Britt; the Barrère-Britt Concertino, a quintet of flute, violin, viola, cello, and piano; and the Barrère Trio, with Britt and pianist Jerome Rappaport. All these groups toured widely, often under the auspices of Community Concerts. As he traveled, Barrère not only brought chamber music to new audiences but provided inspiration to a new generation of musicians. The story is often told that the young Verne Q. Powell, after hearing Barrère play in Chicago, returned to his brother's jewelry shop in Fort Riley, Kansas, to make his first silver flute. Less dramatically, Barrère's concert tours were profitable in recruiting students to Juilliard.

In the chamber orchestra arena, too, Barrère had considerable influence. His skill was not especially with the baton—by many accounts he was an indifferent rehearser and his stick technique was only adequate—but his Little Symphony programs, spanning 1914 to 1941, were paragons of creative programming. He was at once a conservator and an innovator—promoting the baroque and classic-era works of Rameau, Haydn, Mozart, and the like, while introducing American audiences to the compositions of his French contemporaries—André Caplet and Florent Schmitt, for example—and those of his American colleagues, including William Grant Still, Edward MacDowell, and Charles Tomlinson Griffes. He made a point of supporting women composers—Mary Howe, Mabel Wood Hill, and Mabel Wheeler Daniels, to name a few—long before that became fashionable. His programs were eclectic, ranging from the conservatism of Boston classicists such as George Chadwick to the avant-garde idiom of Edgard Varèse—and everything in between. In an era when the vast majority of orchestral players, not to mention conductors, were foreign-born and not sympathetic to American composers, Barrère's advocacy of American music was all the more exceptional.

Barrère owed much of his success to a thorough understanding of his audiences. He recognized their varying tolerances, he provided interesting and different programs, and he made himself a charismatic figure, playing ravishing solos and providing inimitably witty commentaries in calculatedly broken English. Audiences loved his persona of professional Frenchman. One student has described him edging closer and closer to the audience during a solo until he was nearly hanging off the stage; whether or not he always did so literally, he certainly did so figuratively.

One of Barrère's greatest legacies is the establishment of the Paris Conservatoire tradition of woodwind pedagogy in the United States. He taught at the Institute of Musical Art beginning in 1905 and at Juilliard beginning in 1931, and took on many private students as well. Barrère spoke out forcefully in favor of high standards for woodwind teaching. In a letter to Juilliard president John Erskine in 1932, he lamented that "the status of wind instruments... is decidedly too far from that of the string instruments.... In the Paris Conservatoire which I take as a Model...because of its reputation of providing the World with first class wood wind players.... The Examinations are based on the same Standard of work [for winds and strings]." His recommendations were practical and demanding: the provision of first-class instruments for entering students; French-style class instruction; more "practical reading," including the solfeggio system; and guarantees of minimum teaching loads as an incentive for teachers. He also proposed repertoire requirements for all the woodwinds that were taken directly from the Conservatoire competition lists.

Barrère was held in the highest esteem by his students, even when they found his pedagogical methods frustrating—he was a "natural" who sometimes found it difficult to articulate criticisms and suggestions. But, thanks to whatever indescribable medium effective teaching occurs—"osmosis," one student has termed it—they nearly all came away inspired, impressed, and in the end, well instructed, having absorbed at least to some degree the sound he produced and the style he exemplified.

The explanations for Barrère's success are multiple. His excellence as a performer was of course the primary factor. He was intellectually and musically curious, and professionally and musically adventurous. He also had fine entrepreneurial instincts and was skilled at cultivating patrons. His calculation of audiences was keen, and he made savvy use of public relations. He had enormous personal charm, an infectious *joie de vivre*, a marvelous sense of humor, and a generosity that extended to students, composers, colleagues, and audiences alike. He was a celebrity in the best sense of the word, equally at home with Bing Crosby and Mrs. Vincent Astor.

Barrère was, in short, one of the most active and prominent musicians of the first half of this century. No less a figure than Elizabeth Sprague Coolidge once wrote him, "I have always regarded you, as a flutist and a conductor and a program maker, as one of the best influences in our musical life in this country." And the eminent musicologist Carl Engel declared, "France, in letting the great flutist come to America, made an impressive gift of greater significance than when the Statue of Liberty was erected in New York Harbor."

FRANCE

(1876–1905)

1. Photograph, Barrère family, Paris, mid–1880s.

Hortense Barrère

Georges Barrère was the younger of two sons of a French furniture maker, Gabriel François Barrère, and his wife, the former Marie Périne Courtet. This photograph, copied from a sepia *carte de visite,* is the only known image of the family. Georges's older brother Étienne went into the furniture business with his father.

2. Photograph, Paris Conservatoire flute class, 1895. In Claude Dorgeuille, *The French Flute School 1860–1950.* Translated and edited by Edward Blakeman (London: Tony Bingham, 1986), p. 22.

NYPL

Professor Paul Taffanel is seated, center; Philippe Gaubert is to his left. Barrère is fourth from left in the back row; Gaston Blanquart is to his left. Barrère began his Conservatoire studies in 1890 with Henri Altès, but felt that he made no substantial progress until Taffanel took over the class in 1893.

3. Georges Barrère. Typed letter, autographed, to Emil Medicus, Asheville, N.C., November 20, 1923.

Dayton C. Miller Flute Collection, LC

Barrère commented in this letter to the editor of *The Flutist* magazine on the newly published *Méthode Complète de la Flûte* by Paul Taffanel and Philippe Gaubert (Gaubert was Taffanel's successor at the Conservatoire). He wrote, "Absolut[e]ly confidentially (please do not publish this) I think this work has been put together quite hurriedly. I studied with Taffanel and I daresay that next to Gaubert I was his second favorite pupil. I knew all his views about a Method as he talks to me about it very often. Many of the things he told us at the class are absolut[e]ly missing in this book which is supposed to enlist all his methods of teaching and playing. As usual the thing deviated from the subject and became commercial. It was only with a condescending smile that the name of Gariboldi would have been pronounced among his pupils and by himself; nevertheless the name of this more than popular arranger (or rather de-ranger) is recommended in this Method for the very obvious reason that the publisher is the same. With Taffanel I (and many others like D. Maquarre, Laurent etc) have studied the eight books of studies by Joachim Andersen which form a real monument in our literature and no mention of the name of this composer is to be found in this Method."

Another interesting feature of this letter pertains to Barrère's busy schedule in New York. He gives Medicus a statistical summary of his hours from September 1, 1922 to August 31, 1923: 148 rehearsals (370 hours), 167 concerts (334 hours), and 704 lessons (50 pupils, 704 hours). "On top of this you can figure the unnumerable [sic] hours spent in trains, subways, boats, and automobiles not to forget the Teas, Dinners, Suppers, Receptions, Committees and sometimes Concerts to attend."

4. Silver graduation medal of Georges Barrère, Paris Conservatoire, 1895.

Samuel Baron

Barrère won first prize in flute at the Paris Conservatoire in 1895, playing the *Concertstück, Op. 3* by Joachim Andersen. The medal is inscribed: CONSERVATOIRE NATIONAL DE MUSIQUE ET DE DÉCLAMATION / R. F / 1ᴱᴿ PRIX DE FLÛTE / Mᴿ. BARRÈRE / 1895. On the reverse are two allegorical female figures, representing music and drama, and the name of the engraver, J.C. Champlain.

4

5. Gustave Doret. *Temps et Contretemps.* Fribourg: Editions de la Librairie de l'Université, 1942, p. 96.

NYPL

Barrère was first flutist in the orchestra of the Société nationale de musique, conducted by Gustave Doret, for the world premiere of Debussy's *Prélude à l'Après-midi d'une faune* on December 23, 1894. In this letter to the composer, Doret reported [in translation], "I ascend the podium, not without emotion, but very comforted and full of trust. The hall is full. An impressive silence pervades when our marvelous flutist Barrère unrolls his initial theme... All of a sudden, I felt behind my back—it is a particular gift of certain conductors—the public totally subdued! The triumph is complete, so much so that in spite of the rules which forbade the 'encore,' I did not hesitate to break them. And the orchestra, delighted, repeated with joy the work that it had loved and imposed on the overcome public."

6. Société Moderne d'Instruments à Vent, Paris. 10th anniversary booklet; program, Salle des Agriculteurs de France, Paris, February 1, 1905; ticket for same concert.

Dayton C. Miller Flute Collection, LC

In 1895, Barrère foundedthe Société Moderne d'Instruments à Vent, modeled on the Société des Instruments à Vent run by Paul Taffanel from 1879 to 1893. Barrère is listed both as Secrétaire de la Société and as first flutist; Louis Fleury, his good friend and former classmate at the Conservatoire, was the second flutist. In its first ten years, the group played the works of 6 classic and 63 modern composers; played 14 "classic" works and 128 modern works; and premiered 61 works by 40 different composers.

The commemorative booklet includes endorsements and letters of congratulations from such luminaries as Th. Dubois, director of the Conservatoire, Massenet, Saint-Saëns, Ed. Colonne, Alf. Cortot, Alfred Bruneau, Gabriel Fauré, Reynaldo Hahn, Georges Hüe, Vincent D'Indy, Ch. Lefebvre, Gabriel Pierné, and Charles-Marie Widor.

This program was the first concert of the 10th anniversary season; typically, it included five premieres: Vladimir Dyck's quintet for flute, oboe, clarinet, and two bassoons; Francis Thomé's *Thème et Variations* for flute, oboe, clarinet, and bassoon; Carl Reinecke's *Sextuor, Op. 271* for flute,

oboe, two clarinets, horn, and bassoon; and two songs by Philippe Gaubert. Other pieces on the program were Jules Mouquet's *Symphoniette in C, Op. 12,* and Bach's flute sonata in E minor (with Eugène Wagner at the piano).

7. Patrice Devanchy. *Suite pour instruments à vent.* Manuscript score, 1903.

John Solum

The dedication to this four-movement work in D major reads, "A mes amis G. Barrère et L. Leclercq et la Société Moderne d'Instruments à vent." Leclercq was one of the oboists of the Société. The work is scored for woodwind quintet and piano; the third movement, however, is for solo flute and piano.

6

2

WALTER DAMROSCH AND THE NEW YORK SYMPHONY

By 1905, Walter Damrosch had become convinced that his New York Symphony needed an infusion of French woodwind players, whose style he had long preferred and that he particularly envied in the Boston Symphony. As he explained in his autobiography, "The Musical Union, which controlled all orchestral players, had made the influx of good musicians from Europe almost an impossibility by insisting that a player must have lived at least six months in this country before he could join the union, and that until he became a member no other member of the union would be allowed to play with him. I determined therefore to throw down the gantlet to the union by deliberately going to France to engage the five best artists I could find in flute, oboe, clarinet, bassoon, and trumpet, demonstrate their superior excellence to anything we could obtain in New York at that time, and through the pressure of public opinion—and, above all, the necessity of artistic competition with the Boston Symphony—force the union to accept these men as members."

Damrosch sailed to France, and on the advice of Paul Taffanel, he contacted Barrère, who was then fourth flute in the Paris Opéra and a member of the Colonne Orchestra. Indeed, the search for all five players was successful, and he reported to his board that his "Estimate of Frenchmen's Pay" was: Barrère, $2,000; Dubois, $1,400; Tabuteau, $1,200; Leroy, $1,400; Mesnard, $1,400.

However, when the Frenchmen arrived, the union was steadfast in its opposition and allowed them to appear only as soloists. Barrère arrived in New York on May 13, 1905, and made his solo bow with the orchestra on May 20 at the New York Theatre Roof Garden. Damrosch appealed the case to the national union, which allowed the Frenchmen to join the union immediately but fined Damrosch $1,000.

8. Georges Barrère. Autograph letter, signed, to Walter Damrosch, April 18, 1905.

Walter Damrosch Collection, NYPL

In accepting Damrosch's offer, Barrère acknowledged that although the adventure of the conductor's proposal was appealing, he could not abandon the security he had in France without certain conditions: an engagement of one trial year, with a guaranteed minimum salary of 10,000 francs ($2,000), passage for himself and his wife, and admission to the musicians' union.

9. Agreement between the New York Symphony Orchestra Fund Committee of the City of New York and George Barrère, May 20, 1905 (English version).

Walter Damrosch Collection, NYPL

Barrère's contract with the New York Symphony covered his services as "Flute and teacher of flute" for one year beginning May 20, 1905. He was guaranteed minimum earnings of $2,000 per year, payable in weekly installments of $38.46. Barrère agreed "to play in orchestral concerts, chamber music concerts and concerts of every kind, public or private, whenever or wherever required by the [orchestra] and to give lessons on the flute provided, however, that the number of appearances of [Barrère] shall not exceed in value the yearly compensation mentioned above, and this shall be determined according to the following scale of prices:

For a single concert, $8.00

For a weekly engagement in Summer (twice a day) $30.00, in Winter $35.00 (eight times a week)

For hotel expenses for out of town single concert engagements, per day, $1.50

For hotel expenses for out of town weekly concert engagements per week, $10.00

"The remuneration for hotel expenses will not be counted in estimating the minimum earnings mentioned." Barrère also agreed not to accept any other engagements as "Flute and teacher, nor play in any other public or private exhibitions of instrumental music either in public or private without the permission of [the orchestra]." A handwritten addendum states that the orchestra may "prolong this contract for two years longer" if Barrère does not declare his intention before February 1 of wishing to return to Europe—in which case he cannot accept any other engagement in the United States. The contract was indeed extended by two years, to May 20, 1908, under the same conditions.

10. Agreement between the Institute of Musical Art of the City of New York and Walter Damrosch, on behalf of the Trustees of the New York Symphony Orchestra Fund, December 22, 1906.

Walter Damrosch Collection, NYPL

This agreement covered the services of Barrère; Cesare Addimando, oboe; Adolph Dubois, trumpet; Hermann Hand, horn; Leon Leroy, clarinet; and Auguste Mesnard, bassoon, all of whom were obligated by their contracts with the New York Symphony to provide instruction on their instruments at the Institute of Musical Art. This contract obligates Damrosch to guarantee their services for lessons; the Institute was to pay Damrosch $200 for each orchestra player listed. Each teacher's rate would be calculated at $3.00 per hour; if fees for the total amount taught exceeded $200, the IMA was to pay Damrosch any excess sum earned. In effect, Walter Damrosch served as contractor for the Institute, whose director was his brother Frank.

11. [Georges Barrère]. Barrère. New York: privately printed [1928].

NYPL

This spread from Barrère's self-published autobiography reprints a quotation from the autobiography of Walter Damrosch, his mentor and friend, and a photograph of Damrosch signed to Barrère. Damrosch was responsible not only for bringing Barrère to the United States, but also for gaining him election to the Century Club, recommending him for the French Légion d'Honneur, and many other honors. Barrère wrote in his autobiography that he considered the conductor "my dear friend rather than 'My Boss.'"

13

12. Photograph, New York Symphony Orchestra, Carnegie Hall, ca. 1925.

New York Philharmonic Archives

Barrère played first flute in the New York Symphony from 1905 until 1928, except for a one-year leave of absence (1918–19), when he tested a purely freelance existence. (His student, William Kincaid, assumed the principal chair in his absence.) He was a frequent and popular soloist with the orchestra. Barrère left the NYSO when it merged with the New York Philharmonic.

13. Photograph, Georges Barrère and Fitzhugh Haensel, 1916.

Nancy Toff

Emil Mix, a bass player in the New York Symphony, took this snapshot on tour, and it appeared in *Musical Courier* for March 4, 1916. Barrère plays piccolo (actually a fountain pen?) and Fitzhugh W. Haensel, of Haensel & Jones, the orchestra's management, displays his gloved flute technique. Though a serious musician, Barrère was renowned for his sense of humor and his knack for seizing a photo opportunity.

14. [Georges Barrère]. Manuscript program, The New York Symphony Wind Instrument Club.

Walter Damrosch Collection, NYPL

Not long after he joined the New York Symphony, Barrère organized the woodwind players into the New York Symphony Wind Instrument Club. Its personnel included John Roodenburg, flute; Cesare Addimando and Marcel Tabuteau, oboes; Leon Leroy and Arthur Christmann, clarinets; Hermann Hand, horn; and August Mesnard, bassoon. Walter Damrosch joined the chamber group as pianist. This is Barrère's proposal to Damrosch for the group's first program, which they performed on March 7, 1906 at a party organized by Rudolph Schirmer. The repertoire was the *Suite Persane* by André Caplet, the *Trio for flute, bassoon, and piano* by Beethoven; *Preludio e fughetta* and *Pastorale Variée* by Gabriel Pierné; *Two pieces in canonic form* (oboe, clarinets, and piano) by Th. Dubois; and Charles Gounod's *Petite Symphonie*. Barrère recalled in his autobiography, "The program was too long for American audiences."

15. Department of Education, City of New York. New York Symphony Society orchestral scholarships, 1924–25. Mimeographed list.

Walter Damrosch Collection, NYPL

Through the New York City schools, the first-desk men of the New York Symphony offered private lessons, at the teachers' homes, to sixty-two public high school

14

students. Barrère gave his lessons at his apartment, 316 West 93rd Street, on Fridays at 4:00 pm. Among Barrère's students through the NYSO scholarship program was Carmine Coppola, then a student at Stuyvesant High School. He went on to study with Barrère at the Institute (1926–30), later becoming a member of the Detroit Symphony and principal flute of the NBC Symphony under Toscanini before attaining fame as a film composer.

16. Photograph, Georges Barrère teaching Marjorie Klugherz, New York, December 22, 1923.

Nancy Toff, gift of Mrs. Walter Coleman

One of Barrère's students through the NYSO scholarship program was Marjorie Klugherz, a student at Bay Ridge High School in Brooklyn.

17. New York Symphony Orchestra gold cufflinks.

Leonard Sharrow

When the New York Symphony merged with the New York Philharmonic in 1928, Barrère refused to play second flute to anyone—or even to share the first chair with the Philharmonic principal, John Amans. Henry Harkness Flagler, longtime patron of the Symphony, gave a farewell dinner for the departing players and presented each with a pair of gold cufflinks engraved with the player's initials and dates of service. In his acceptance speech, Barrère quipped, "You give us cufflinks, but you take the shirts off our backs." This pair of cufflinks belonged to Saul Sharrow, a violinist in the New York Symphony and concertmaster of the Barrère Little Symphony.

MUSIC BY BARRÈRE

18. Georges Barrère. *Nocturne* **for flute and piano. New York: G. Schirmer, 1913.**

Frances Blaisdell

This is Barrère's only original composition for flute. It is dedicated "À la mémoire de mon cher Maître P. Taffanel."

19. Georges Barrère. *Chanson d'automne* **for voice and piano. Words by Paul Verlaine. English version by Henry Chapman. New York: G. Schirmer, 1915. Composer's autographed presentation copy to David Bispham, November 25, 1915.**

NYPL

This is Barrère's only published song and is dedicated to the French tenor Edmond Clément. This copy is inscribed to the baritone David Bispham, with whom Barrère had collaborated in a concert of American music the previous year.

20. Georges Barrère. *In the Vegetable Garden.* **Trio for Nine Instruments (perhaps ten). Manuscript score.**

LC

The full attribution on this score, in Barrère's hand, is "by Georges Barrère in collaboration with Mendelssohn, St Saens, Massenet, Haydn, Bizet, Rossini, and others." It is dedicated to Walter Damrosch.

Barrère's press agent cited this piece, along with *Symphony Digest*, as evidence of Barrère's light touch in programming for his Little Symphony. The work is in six movements: *String Beans (Fileuse),* for flute/piccolo, English horn, and saxophone in E-flat (based on Mendelssohn's *Songs without Words*); *Lettuce (My heart at thy dear voice),* for alto flute in G, oboe d'amore in A, and E-flat clarinet (based on the aria from Saint-Saëns' *Samson and Delilah*); *Onion (O Dry thy tears),* for flute, oboe, and saxophone in E-flat; *Tomato (La Surprise),* for piccolo, oboe, and clarinet in E-flat (based on Haydn's *Surprise Symphony*); *Cauliflower (Flower Song),* for flute, piano (played by the flutist's right hand), English horn, and clarinet in B-flat (based on the "Flower Song" from Bizet's *Carmen*); and *Garlic (The Lost Rose),* for piccolo, oboe d'amore, and saxophone (based on *O sole mio,* a *Tarantelle* by Rossini, and *The Last Rose of Summer*).

21. Cadenza to J. J. Quantz, *Concerto in G Major* **for flute, second movement. Manuscript, 1933.**

Frances Blaisdell

Barrère wrote this cadenza for Frances Blaisdell's performance of the concerto with the Juilliard orchestra in 1933. G. Schirmer published Barrère's cadenzas for the first time in 1994, as part of Frances Blaisdell's edition of the full concerto.

22. Georges Barrère. Cadenza for W. A. Mozart, Concerto in G, K. 313, third movement. Manuscript.

Bernard Goldberg

23. Georges Barrère. Cadenzas for the Concerto in G Major, K. 313, by Mozart. New York: Galaxy Music, 1943.

Nancy Toff

24. Georges Barrère. Cadenzas for the Concerto in D Major, K. 314, by Mozart. New York: Galaxy Music, 1939.

Nancy Toff

Barrère notes in the score to the D major cadenzas, "In my cadenzas to the first and second movements I have quoted briefly from the cadenzas written by Joachim Andersen for this Concerto." He wrote out cadenzas for a number of his students (Ruth Freeman has a manuscript for the cadenzas of the D major concerto). They were later published in essentially the same form by Galaxy.

25. Antonin Dvorak, arr. Georges Barrère. *American Quartet,* arranged for woodwind quintet. Manuscript score.

Samuel Baron

Barrère made quite a few arrangements for woodwind quintet. Twelve of them were published by G. Schirmer, and an arrangement of Poldowski's *Suite Miniature* was published by Galaxy. Two unpublished quintet arrangements are known to exist; the other is a setting of a Haydn piano trio.

MUSIC DEDICATED TO BARRÈRE

Throughout his career, Barrère worked closely with composers. He was involved with the Society for the Publication of American Music and pointed proudly to this involvement in the promotional literature for his Little Symphony and in his correspondence.

26. Seth Bingham. *Suite for winds, Op. 17.* **Manuscript score.**

Seth Bingham Collection, NYPL.

Seth Bingham (1882–1972) joined the Yale music faculty in 1908, later taught at Columbia and Union Theological Seminary, and was organist of Madison Avenue Presbyterian Church in New York. The *Suite for winds* is scored for 2 flutes, oboe, 2 clarinets, 2 horns, and 2 bassoons and is dedicated to Barrère. It was premiered by the Barrère Ensemble on February 2, 1914 (see catalog no. 27). Bingham's humorous *Tame Animal Tunes, Op. 20* was often performed by the Barrère Little Symphony.

27. Program, The Barrère Ensemble of Wind Instruments, Belasco Theatre, [New York], February 2, 1914.

NYPL

In addition to the premiere of Seth Bingham's *Suite for winds, Op. 17,* the program included Vladimir Dyck's *First Symphony;* four songs; the premiere of Mabel Wood Hill's *Two Pieces, Intermezzo* and *Gypsy Dance,* for flute, oboe, English horn, and pairs of clarinets, horns, and bassoons; and Florent Schmitt's *Lied and Scherzo, Op. 54.* Members of the ensemble were Barrère and Rocco Guerriere, flutes; Irving Cohn, English horn; Bruno Labate, oboe; Josef Franzel and Frederick Dultgen, French horns; Gustave Langenus and Frederick Van Amburgh, clarinets; and Ugo Savolini and Emile Barbot, bassoons. Basso Herbert Witherspoon and pianist Charles A. Baker assisted.

28. John Parsons Beach. *Naive Landscapes.* **Manuscript score, for flute, oboe, clarinet, and piano.**

John Parsons Beach Collection/NYPL

John Parsons Beach (1877–1953) studied piano with Harold Bauer in Paris and composition with Charles Martin Loeffler. He composed a variety of ballets and orchestral and chamber works in an essentially late Romantic style. *Naive Landscapes* is scored for flute, oboe, clarinet, and piano, and is

27

in four movements: I. I heard the waters telling their beads; II. The Little Fellow; III. Fairy Piper; IV. Summer Night. It is dedicated to Paul Mowrer.

29. Program, Barrère Ensemble. Aeolian Hall, [New York], February 13, 1920.

Nancy Toff, from the estate of Arthur Lora

The Barrère Ensemble premiered John Beach's *Naive Landscapes* at this concert, with the composer at the piano. Also on the program were the probable New York premiere of Beethoven's *Sextette in E Flat* (2 clarinets, 2 horns, 2 bassoons); the New York premiere of Gabriel Pierné's *Preludio e Fughetta, Op. 40, No. 1* (2 flutes, oboe, clarinet, horn, 2 bassoons); the second New York performance of Pierné's *Pastorale Variée (in the Olden Style), Op. 30* (flute, oboe, clarinet, horn, trumpet, 2 bassoons); the New York premiere of Pierre Bucquet's *Suite for Two Flutes*; and the second New York performance of Georges Enesco's *Dixtuor* (2 flutes, oboe, English horn, 2 clarinets, 2 horns, 2 bassoons). This was not, technically, the New York premiere of the Pierné; the New York Symphony Wind Instrument Club had played it in a private concert in 1906 (see catalog no. 14), but this was apparently the first public performance.

30. Charles T. Griffes. *Poem.* Manuscript score, 1918.

NYPL

31. Announcement of New York Symphony Orchestra program, November 16, 1919, from Aeolian Hall program.

NYPL

Barrère premiered the *Griffes Poem* with the New York Symphony Orchestra, Walter Damrosch conducting, on November 16, 1919, in Aeolian Hall. W. J. Henderson wrote the following review in the *New York Sun* (November 17, 1919): "It is not only a brilliant solo for flute, but is a very pleasing composition, disclosing musical temperament, as well as mastery of materials." Katherine Lane wrote in the *Evening Mail*: "It was a sort of Oriental pastoral that the poem by Charles Griffes suggested.... Possibly this was partly due to George Barrère... since that bearded gentleman has much of the dignity of a sultan." The *New York Tribune* said: "Compositions for the flute even when played by such a splendid musician as Georges Barrère, do not as a rule give rise to wild enthusiasm, yet, yesterday's audience applauded the work and the soloist for several minutes. The poem is a composition of such grace and variety of expression, rich in melodic ideas and written with an unusual feeling both for the solo instrument and for the orchestra. If Americans can but continue to produce such works, all talk of the unrequited native composer will be speedily set at rest Mr. Griffes is a composer who will bear watching. Mr. Barrère, needless to say, gave a beautiful performance of the solo flute...."

Barrère made a piano reduction of the orchestra score that was published by G. Schirmer in 1922. He first performed this transcription, with Walter Golde at the piano, at a Barrère Ensemble concert on February 15, 1921.

32. Georges Barrère. Autograph letter, signed, to Emil Medicus, June 11, [1921].

Dayton C. Miller Flute Collection, LC

In this letter to the editor of *The Flutist* magazine, Barrère notes that the *Poem* was one of several solos he played on the recent western tour of the Little Symphony. "About this latter work I am just finishing a work ordered to me by Schirmer. It is a work where I have to put more than music, Ch. T. Griffes; when he died 14

months ago didn't leave any complete piano score of his Poem for flute and orch. I have his manuscript notes of it which are not all that he used to play when rehearsing with me. I have to use my memory and it puts me back to the lovely time we used to have working with such a delightful musician. His Poem will be soon published with piano acct. by Schirmer and I hope every flute player will welcome this beautiful work with the same enthusiasm than [sic] the audiences for which I have played it in New York,—San Francisco—Los Angeles."

33. David Stanley Smith. *Fête galante. Fantasy for Flute and Piano, Op. 48.* 1921, revised 1930. Piano reduction by the composer. Manuscript score and part.

LC

34. Symphony Society Bulletin. Vol. XV, No. 4, December 5, 1921.

NYPL

David Stanley Smith (1877–1949), then dean of the Yale School of Music and conductor of the New Haven Symphony, was a

protégé of Horatio Parker and also studied with Widor. He began work on *Fête Galante* in December 1920, completing it on February 2, 1921. It was dedicated to Barrère, who premiered it with the New York Symphony, Walter Damrosch conducting, on December 11, 1921. It was later performed by Georges Laurent with the Boston Symphony, Pierre Monteux conducting, in April 1923.

Philip Hale's notes for the Boston performances quote the composer: "The 'Fête Galante' is intended to give a picture of aristocratic life in France, as portrayed by Watteau. Many of the paintings of Watteau are of the style known as the '*fête galante.*' In these pictures the subjects are polite gatherings of ladies in silks and courtiers with musical instruments, in a setting of rich gardens and fountains. The music is a sequence of hints and fragments rather than a formal development of themes. One of the motives suggests a waltz. This is of course, anachronistic in a picture of eighteenth-century France; but the composer believes it is not out of place in his musical scheme, since the music is meant to reflect the spirit and color of the *fête galante,* without regard to details of time and place....

"Though the flute predominates at all times in the composition, there is so much subtlety in the accompaniment as to justify the designation 'for orchestra with flute obbligato.' There are important solo passages for violin, viola, harp, and wind instruments. The work is actually a piece of chamber music, as may be expected of music for so delicate an instrument as the flute."

35. Mabel Wheeler Daniels. *Deep Forest. Prelude for Little Symphony Orchestra, Op. 31, No. 1.* New York: J. Fischer & Bro., 1932. Score.

NYPL

Mabel Wheeler Daniels (1879–1971), who studied composition with George Chadwick in Boston and Ludwig Thuille in Germany, was one of several women composers whose works Barrère performed. The piece is dedicated "To the Barrère Little Symphony." Barrère later performed her *Pastoral Ode,* Op. 40, for flute and strings.

Daniels recalled, in an unpublished memoir, that she had the good fortune to meet Barrère at the 1930 Worcester Festival, and he invited her to send this score to him for an imminent reading session in New York. The piece was originally scored for strings, solo woodwinds, two horns, percussion, and harp. When Barrère protested that he had no harp, Daniels suggested arranging the harp part for clarinet and re-arranging the woodwinds. She reported receiving frosty stares from the male composers at the reading session, but Barrère decided to premiere the piece at the next Town Hall concert, on April 5, 1931. The Little Symphony played it many times on tour in the U.S., Canada, and Havana. It subsequently was played by the Chicago and Los Angeles Women's Symphony Orchestras, by Arthur Fiedler and members of the Boston Symphony, and, in an expanded version, by Hans Kindler, Serge Koussevitzky, and Sir John Barbirolli.

36. Georges Barrère. Typed letter, signed, to [Mabel Wheeler] Daniels, June 19, 1933.

Mabel Wheeler Daniels Collection, Schlesinger Library, Radcliffe College

Barrère encloses the program for his August 8 concert at Chautauqua, at which he plans to conduct *Deep Forest.* "Last winter I received the new score with a very kind MS inscription and I am pretty sure I thanked you for it in due time(?) Now what is going to happen for the separate parts? Am I to ask Fischer to lend them to me and pay all kind of publisher, composer etc. fees on them. I told you that I didnt [sic] want to figure as an arranger. That was a joke; but after all I think Mr Fischer must realize that I am the first performer of the Deep Forest and perhaps he will waive his rights for fee. You know that [C]hautauqua doesnt pay much royalties and that I dont do that at all out of my much reduced salary. But I am most anxious to play Deep Forest if these material difficulties can be spared. By the way I have a larger orchestra in Chautauqua than my regular Little Symph. For instance I have two horns and two trpts. Naturally I wont double up on these instruments unless you suggest one or two places to that effect, but I have three first violins and that will mean two part[s]. I shall use my own discretion about divisi. I also have 2 seconds and 2 violas. Kindly let me know about the material. If you allow me to do so I can arrange the original material to fit the new score, that will means [sic] a re-writing of the whole second section from your first change. It might save money and time, if not trouble for me."

37. Flyer, Barrère Little Symphony, 1929–30 season.

NYPL

In 1929–30 Barrère celebrated the 25th anniversary of his arrival in the United States. In announcing three concerts by his chamber orchestra, he noted in a letter to potential subscribers, "I shall try to justify this bold extravaganza by some ultra-interesting programs. Dear old antiques will be programmed alongside of composers scarcely out of their teens.... Please look at the program: out of 20 names of composers, eight are American and out of these eight, two are women!!!" Those two were Mary Howe of New York and Washington, D.C., whose *Mists* was slated for its world premiere on March 23, and Ethel G. Hier of Cincinnati, whose *Choreography* was slated for premiere on March 30.

Other premieres that season were the U.S. premiere of the Roussel *Trio* for flute, viola, and cello (which Barrère had given its world premiere in October 1929 in Prague; see catalog no. 91); August Fickenscher's *Variations "Dies Irae"*; the American premiere of Villa-Lobos's *Choros No. 2* for flute and clarinet; the world premiere of William Grant Still's *Africa Sym-*

phony, and Joseph Hüttel's *L'Arlequinade,* "a little dancing Suite for 13 musicians." After Barrère played the premiere of Hüttel's *Divertissement Grotesque* in October 1929 (see catalog no. 66), Hüttel gratefully sent him the piece for chamber orchestra. Also promised was the second New York performance of Wallingford Riegger's *Impressions for flute alone* [the *Suite, Op. 8*].

38. Wallingford Riegger. *Divertissement, Op. 15,* for flute, harp, and cello. Manuscript score, 1933.

Wallingford Riegger Collection, NYPL

Riegger's trio was written for and dedicated to Barrère-Salzedo-Britt.

39. Wallingford Riegger. Performance register, 1917–1960.

Wallingford Riegger Collection, NYPL

Riegger methodically recorded the performance histories of his works, indicating here the premiere of the *Divertissement* by Barrère-Salzedo-Britt on December 11, 1933, at the New School. He also lists four 1934 performances of the work by Barrère-Salzedo-Britt: February 5, The Bohemians, New York; February 11, Washington [at the home of Elizabeth Sprague Coolidge]; May 8, Town Hall, New York; and November 28, Philadelphia Society for Contemporary Music. On earlier pages he lists Barrère's premiere of his *Suite for solo flute, Op. 8* on February 2, 1930, at the League of Composers, New York and a subsequent performance on June 15 at the Maverick Concerts, Woodstock, New York (see catalog no. 125).

40. Flyer, Concert of American Music, New School for Social Research, [New York], December 11, [1933].

Wallingford Riegger Collection, NYPL

In addition to the premiere of the Riegger *Divertissement,* the program included Carl

40

Ruggles's *Angels* (in a version for 6 flutes) and Henry Brant's *Concerto for flute with the accompaniment of 10 flutes* (later known as *Angels and Devils*). Fritz Reiner had been scheduled to conduct, but was away on tour, so Barrère and Brant took his place. The other performers were Horace Britt, cello; Isador Freed, piano; Harry Kaufman, piano; Carlos Salzedo, harp; and ten of Barrère's flute students.

Musical America reported (December 25, 1933): "Enthusiastic applause caused a repetition of the last movement." The *New York World Telegram* (December 12, 1933) called the Riegger "a Pandora's box of surprises that included the buzzing device of inserting a strip of paper among the strings of the harp. The masterly playing of the new ensemble transmuted Mr. Riegger's coiling atonalities into a glittering chain of sound.... For Mr. Brant's novel concerto for flute, ... ten flutists ranged behind Mr. Barrère, the soloist, and followed the composer's baton like model pupils."

The *New York Herald Tribune* (December 12, 1933) said of the Ruggles, which had previously been heard in versions for six trumpets and six violins, "Its greatest merit is its brevity." It termed the Riegger trio "largely an experiment in total combinations for the three instruments. The first movement often sounded like an attempt to bring parts of Strauss's 'Till Eulenspiegel' up to the minute, harmonically."

25

41. Flyer, New Music Quarterly Recordings, 1934.

Wallingford Riegger Collection, NYPL

In 1934 NMQR announced its recording NMQ 1012A, which included the third movement of the Riegger trio played by Barrère-Salzedo-Britt. It was recorded on December 31, 1933. The following year NMQR planned to issue two movements from the *Suite for woodwind quintet, Op. 11* (1930) by Nicolai Berezowsky (1900–1953), and the *Suite for woodwind quintet* (1934) by Henry Cowell, played by the Barrère woodwind quintet (Barrère; Carlos Mullenix, oboe; Fred Van Amburgh, clarinet; Angel Del Busto, bassoon; Rudolph Puletz, horn). These pieces were recorded in early 1935; later that year NMQR issued a recording of Walter Piston's *Three Pieces for Flute, Clarinet, and Bassoon* (1926), NMQ 1113, with a subset of the same personnel.

Marshall Kernochan, reviewing the Riegger disc in *Musical America* in July 1934, said that "The recording and the individual performances are excellent," but "The music here presented is, in our opinion, the offspring of the midnight oil and of the wanderings of the intellectual nomad, who, having abjured human feelings, is now without a tangible goal. Not even the high art of such men as Messrs. Barrère, Salzedo and Britt, who play the Riegger piece, can save it." The Finale, Kernochan wrote, "is apparently devised to explore the gamut of sounds obtainable by these instruments when playing in various unnatural manners. No other conceivable musical purpose of any kind could be detected by the reviewer; but, no doubt, the peculiar thumpings in the harp, the sudden clucks and squeals of the flute, and the wild leaps indulged in by the 'cello, were of absorbing technical interest to Mr. Riegger."

42. Bernard Wagenaar. Scrapbook. 1938–42.

The Juilliard School Archives

Dutch-born Bernard Wagenaar (1894–1971) taught composition at Juilliard. An active member of the League of Composers, he received commissions from the New York Philharmonic and other organizations. He wrote his *Triple Concerto for flute, harp, cello and orchestra* for Barrère-Salzedo-Britt, to whom it is dedicated, and the trio gave the initial performances with the Philadelphia Orchestra, Eugene Ormandy conducting, at the Academy of Music on March 18 and 19, 1938. They repeated their performance with the Philadelphia at Carnegie Hall the following week, and on May 20, 1941, with the NBC Symphony conducted by Ormandy, as part of the first festival held in America by ISCM. The latter concert was broadcast live on NBC radio.

In the notes for the premiere, the composer recalled, "While walking one day, my friend Salzedo suggested that this chamber-music combination might be projected even more strikingly by combining it with that magnificent instrument, the modern orchestra, and he asked me if I would write a work in the form of a Triple Concerto.... For the sake of both special interest and utmost brilliance, I have asked Mr. Salzedo to compose the Harp-Cadenza, and suggested to Messrs. Barrère and Britt to elaborate a few of my own ideas into their respective Cadenzas...."

Henry Pleasants' review of the premiere appeared in the *Philadelphia Evening Bulletin* (March 19, 1938): "Mr. Wagenaar is a cultivated and accomplished musician, and passages of his score have a pleasant lyric quality and show ingenuity and insight in orchestration. But there is little body to the work and less sustained movement. It is obviously a piece of convenience, made to order for the Barrère-Salzedo-Britt trio, rather than a work in which the instrumental combination was dictated by a musical conception...." Olin Downes wrote in the *New York Times* (March 23, 1938), "The concerto's defect is that it is twice too long. This is regrettable, since its merits are so pronounced."

5

THE PLATINUM FLUTE

The platinum flute made for Barrère by the Wm. S. Haynes Co. is one of the most famous instruments in modern flute history. It was not, as is commonly believed, the first platinum flute, but it is the first all-platinum flute and the first platinum flute made in the United States. The London firm of Rudall, Carte & Co. had made three platinum flutes by the summer of 1935. They used pure platinum, no alloys, whereas Haynes used 10% irridium. Rudall, Carte also employed a silver mechanism to minimize the weight, whereas Haynes used the same platinum alloy for the keys as well as the body. Rudall, Carte took its first order for a platinum flute in November 1933, from a customer for whom the firm had previously made a platinum headjoint. The International Nickel Company press release said, "Some player in England is understood to have had a platinum flute made for his personal use about a year ago, but Mr. Barrère is the first concert artist to use one in a public performance." That official debut took place on July 28, 1935; Barrère played the Bach *Suite in B minor* with the Chautauqua Symphony Orchestra.

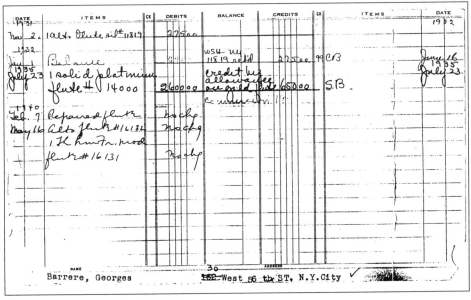

43

43. Wm. S. Haynes Co. Georges Barrère customer card from New York office.

Wm. S. Haynes Co.

The Wm. S. Haynes Co. records reflect Barrère's purchase of his platinum flute, No. 14000, for $2,600, on July 23, 1935. He was allowed a $650 credit for his 14K gold flute (No. 9540), which he had purchased on February 24, 1927, for $450. The flute weighed 17.5 ounces and had a footjoint to B-natural.

44

44. Photograph, Georges Barrère and xWm. S. Haynes, Wm. S. Haynes Co. office, ca. mid–1930s.

Nancy Toff, gift of Lewis J. Deveau, Wm. S. Haynes Co.

Barrère had a long relationship with the Haynes Company; he first purchased a Haynes flute in 1913. His portrait appears prominently in its catalogs as early as 1916; in that year's catalog, for instance, his signature is at the top of a page of signature endorsements from leading flutists of the day. Barrère certainly collected commissions on flutes purchased by his students, and may well have had further financial interests in the firm's production of silver flutes, whose success is in large part attributable to his advocacy of the silver flute. The Haynes production logs record 25 flutes sold to Barrère; in fact, he owned several others that were purchased from other sources, and some of those 25 were resold to students.

45. *The Platinum Flute and Georges Barrère* [pamphlet]. New York: [International Nickel Company], November 1935.

Nancy Toff

This pamphlet was prepared by W.H. Baldwin of the International Nickel Company; in November 1935 he sent it to Dayton C. Miller for his comments. It reads in part:

"Convinced that the platinum flute is the best he has ever played or heard, Mr. Barrère has already assisted in making scientific tests of its tone at the Bell Telephone Laboratories. These consisted of blowing the note "G" in the lower register and "G" in the middle register on a 14-karat gold flute, a sterling silver flute and the platinum flute, into a microphone connected with an electrical instrument which analyzed the components of the sound. Repeated tests of each flute enabled the laboratory experts to assert that with the platinum flute in the lower register the odd harmonics were richer, and in the middle register, although there was not so marked a difference, the same tendency toward richness was observed in the even harmonics. Direct tests of the resonance of such metals as platinum, gold, silver and steel show that annealed iridium-platinum, the material of the Barrère flute, is highly resonant.

"Summarizing the reasons why he prefers the platinum flute to any other he has ever played, Mr. Barrère recently said he was convinced that the platinum flute owes its superiority to the material of which it is made. He stated that the instrument had greater brilliancy in the high register, a somewhat higher 'speaking quality,' which enabled him to obtain better legato and prompter response in long intervals. He also discovered that this flute seemed to maintain an even warmth through long concerts, even out of doors, a factor of great value in insuring perfect pitch. He felt, in addition, that both the volume and the quality of the tone were better in the platinum flute than in other flutes, despite the fact that ordinarily when volume is increased, quality suffers and vice versa."

46. Georges Barrère. Invitation to an intimate concert and discussion of his new platinum flute, Sherry's, New York, November 20 [1935].

Dayton C. Miller Flute Collection, LC

"Mr. Georges Barrère requests the honor of your presence at an intimate concert and your participation in a discussion of his new platinum flute at Sherry's, 300 Park Avenue, on Wednesday afternoon November twentieth at four-thirty o'clock." The guests included a number of prominent musicians, including Eddy Brown, Henry Hadley, Louis Hasselmans, Edgard Varèse, David Mannes, Victor Harris, Mrs. Albert Stoessel, Archer Gibson, Walter Kramer, Maurice Jacquet, Dr. Carlton Sprague Smith, Frederick Jagel, Marshall Kernochan, and Germaine Schnitzer.

47. Program, Georges Barrère, flutist, assisted by Rachel Morton, soprano; Alice Nichols, piano. Sherry's, [New York], November 20, 1935.

Dayton C. Miller Flute Collection, LC

The program is a classic Barrère flute recital, beginning with the Bach E major sonata but consisting primarily of French repertoire. It includes his own flute-and-piano arrangements of Gluck's *Scene from "Orpheus"* (his signature piece) and André Wormser's *Madrigal.* Dayton C. Miller noted on his copy that Barrère added a piece with piano accompaniment by Walter Damrosch, which was Ravel's *La Flûte Enchantée.* In fact, Damrosch accompanied the entire last group on the program.

After the music, there were scientific comments by E. C. Wente of Bell Telephone Laboratories; Frederick E. Carter, research metallurgist of the Baker & Co. precious metals refinery, Newark, New Jersey; and A. J. Wadhams, vice president in charge of research, International Nickel Company.

48. "$3,000 Flute," *Time,* December 2, 1935, p. 23.

Nancy Toff

The newsmagazine noted Barrère's pioneering action in playing a silver flute, not the then-prevalent wood instrument, when he first arrived in the United States. "Ten years ago he took to playing on a $1,000 gold flute" (*Time* was off by a mere 100%); last week he demonstrated a flute made of platinum. Price: $3,000.... Mr. Barrère plays any flute so expertly, transmits so much personal charm to his audience, that those who heard him last week, tootling away between two potted palms in a salon at Sherry's, wondered whether they were being impressed by the player or the instrument." But, *Time* reported definitively, scientists from the Bell Telephone Laboratories had declared platinum superior to silver or gold.

49. Edgard Varèse. *Density 21.5* for solo flute. New Music, 1936. Score, autographed to Frances Blaisdell by the composer.

Frances Blaisdell

Barrère asked Edgard Varèse to compose a piece for the new platinum flute. Its title is based on the density of platinum, 21.5; Barrère's flute, made of a platinum/irridium alloy, actually had a density of 21.6. *Density 21.5* was the first piece for flute to employ audible key slaps. Barrère had been a supporter of Varèse's music for many years; the Barrère Little Symphony gave the second New York performance of his *Offrandes* on March 18, 1928 (see catalog no. 75).

50. Program, Gala Concert for the Endowment Fund of the Lycée Français de New York, Carnegie Hall, February 26, 1936. Lily Pons, Lucienne Boyer, Gaby Casadesus, Barrère, Salzedo, Britt, Robert Casadesus, Léon Rothier; Louis Hasselmans, master of ceremonies; Maurice Jacquet, piano.

Carnegie Hall Archives

51. Photograph, Louis Hasselmans, Georges Barrère, Edgard Varèse, Lili Pons, Léon Rothier. In Hilda Jolivet, *Varèse* (Paris: Hachette, 1973).

NYPL

Barrère premiered *Density 21.5* on February 16, 1936, at a benefit concert for the endowment fund of the Lycée Francais of New York. The program opened with *La Timide* and *Tambourin* by Rameau and *Serenade for the Doll* and *Golliwog's Cakewalk* by Debussy, all played by Barrère-Salzedo-Britt. Several vocal sets followed, and then Hüe's *Fantaisie,* Varèse's *Density 21.5,* and Godard's *Allegretto.* Salzedo, Pons, and the Casadesuses completed the program. The program states, "Density 21.5 was composed especially for this occasion and dedicated to Georges Barrère."

52. W. H. Baldwin, International Nickel Co., 67 Wall Street, New York, typed letter, signed, to Dayton C. Miller, September 24, 1935.

Dayton C. Miller Flute Collection, LC

Baldwin reminded Miller, a physicist expert in acoustical matters and an avid flute collector, that they had corresponded about Miller undertaking experiments with platinum flute tubes. (Miller had begun such research in 1904 but had sold the tubes during World War I.) Baldwin reports that he has heard that Haynes made a platinum flute for Barrère, has visited Barrère in Woodstock, and has arranged for the flute to be tested by the Bell Telephone Laboratories. Baldwin invites Miller's comments.

The *Cleveland Plain Dealer* reported, incorrectly, that Dr. Miller developed the platinum flute in the belief that denser metal would impart "softer and mellower tones" to the flute. In fact, Miller did examine the flute at the Haynes shop in December 1935 and made detailed notes of its dimensions/specifications. Miller did not want his name associated with the flute, and complained to Rudall, Carte & Co., "I think the makers of the flute here have tried to capitalize my interest in connection with the flute for the sake of publicity. I assure you that I am not responsible in any way for any of the statements."

53. Georges Barrère. Typed letter to [Everett Timm], November 29, 1941.

Everett Timm

Three months after suffering a stroke, Barrère typed this letter to his former Woodstock student Everett Timm, detailing the grim results of his illness. He advises Timm about the purchase of a flute; his facility with English, as well as typing, declined markedly after the stroke (August 22). "In matter of flutes I am always very reluctant to give advice without seeing the instrument, which will be useless now because I cannot play yet. If the instrument seem so good to you buy it. You will have the be[n]efit of an old gold flute rather than a gold with silver keys. In general there is no trouble putting a B foot on a flute originally constructed with a C foot, though the makers themselves are opposed to this. My old Lot was originally built with C, when I get it second hand it had a B foot joint and I play the instrument for more than 30 years. As platinum with silve[r] keys I quite against it. I dont [sic] believe in two metals. And platinum is not any better than silver. This is confidential, of course."

Barrère's true opinion of the platinum flute is confirmed by former students and members of the Little Symphony, who recall that Barrère would switch back to a silver flute when no one could tell.

6

EARLY YEARS IN AMERICA

54. Program, Georges Barrère, flutist; Hermann Martonne, violinist; George Rogovoy, violoncellist; Madam M. B. Barrère, mezzo soprano [Waukegan, Illinois, July 1908].

Hortense Barrère

Barrère's first wife, Michelette Burani, was a mezzo-soprano. Her father had been in the management of the Folies Bergère in Paris, where Barrère played in the orchestra. For several summers (1905–10), the New York Symphony (listed here as the Walter Damrosch Orchestra) was in residence at the Ravinia Festival outside Chicago and performed in other area venues. This program lists an upcoming performance by the orchestra with the same soloists as at the recital, at the Schwartz Theatre, sponsored by the Waukegan Conservatory of Music. The musicians apparently gave some chamber recitals as well. This is one of several occasions on which Barrère and his wife performed together.

The couple was divorced in 1913, and Michelette Burani went on to a successful career as a character actress on Broadway, performing with Alfred Lunt, Helen Hayes, and others.

55. Program, Joint Recital, Georges Barrère, flute, and Ernest Consolo, piano. Belasco Theatre, [New York], March 2, [1913].

NYPL

Barrère was the first person to popularize the flute recital in the United States. This program included the Bach *Sonata in A Major,* Schubert's *Introduction and Variations Concertantes, Op. 160,* and the Pierné sonata.

56. Program, Exposition of Classical and Modern Chamber Music 1916–17, Program IV.

NYPL

From 1907 to 1930, harpsichordist and pianist Arthur Whiting organized a series of concert-lectures at American universities, focusing particularly on baroque literature, which was then quite unusual. The first performances were at Princeton, Yale, and Harvard; the program later expanded to Wesleyan, Hamilton, and MIT. Barrère was involved in these concerts for many years, and also played frequently in private

31

concerts at Whiting's New York studio. In the 1916–17 season, Barrère participated in the fourth of the five concerts, along with Fernanda Pratt, contralto; Arkady Bourstin, violin; Marco Peyrot, cello; and Whiting, harpsichord. The program consisted of Gluck's *Sonata in G minor* (flute, violin, cello, harpsichord); Aubert's *Air in D* and Marcello's *Sonata in F* (flute and harpsichord); and Ariosti's *Cantate, "Il Naufragio"* (contralto, flute, violin, cello, harpsichord). The program was performed at Princeton, February 23; Yale, February 26; and Harvard, March 1.

57. Georges Barrère. "Violin of the Woodwind Instruments." Translated by R. Champion. *Musical America,* November 6, 1909, p. 9.

NYPL

In this article Barrère discusses why the strings should not be considered superior to the winds. He describes the Paris Conservatoire's custom of commissioning composers to write *concours* pieces "for those instruments least favored in the current repertoire.... As a result of this policy there is now not a single instrument that can complain of the lack of a piece of real music.

"In this list of new music one must admit that the flute has been particularly favored.... the literature of the flute already quite rich in classics, continues to augment from day to day.... I know that one kapellmeister of the greatest eminence considers the flute as the violin, so to speak, of the wood winds, and consequently the flutist as a kind of concertmeister.

"It is a misfortune ... that numbers of flutists, who enjoy but rarely the opportunity of appearing as soloists, should choose for such occasions pieces known as 'brilliant' in the archives of the old repertoire. They delude themselves by believing that the modern public, whose musical discrimination becomes more acute from day to day, can still be made to take an interest in pompous variations and the ancient acrobatics of the instrument, so greatly valued by our forbears of sixty years ago. These monstrosities, as we regard them today, are dead beyond revival. Written as a rule by flautists, and remarkably well adapted to the instrument, their intrinsic poverty excludes all but a legacy of superannuated interest. To play persistently a repertoire of this character, to call up the lifeless skeletons of a past, alike sterile and *baroque,* is effectually to coerce public sentiment to the conviction that the flute is scarcely to be regarded as a *musical* instrument."

Barrère implores, "This charming instrument, consolation of the great, eulogized by the poets—this instrument bearing thus in its limpid tones the sanction of the sentiment of the ages, is it not fitted for loftier things than velocity and mere virtuosity?" The classical composers, he notes, from Bach through the modern French school, "seem to have thought so."

58. "Honored for Ten Years' Service to American Music," *Musical America,* June 5, 1915, p. 33.

NYPL

It took Barrère very little time to become a fixture of the New York musical establishment. On May 20, 1915, the tenth anniversary of his American debut, he was feted at a dinner at the Café des Beaux Arts in New York. Walter Damrosch and David Mannes made speeches; Damrosch, Henry Harkness Flagler (chief patron of the New York Symphony), and members of the orchestra presented Barrère with a loving cup, and members of the Barrère Ensemble sent a large laurel wreath. Among those in attendance were violinist Alexander Saslavsky, composer Howard Brockway, cellist Paul Kéfer, and clarinetist Frederick Van Amburgh, manager of the Little Symphony.

59. Photograph, Georges Barrère and sons Gabriel and Claude, New York, ca. 1916.

Hortense Barrère

59

Georges and Michelette Barrère had two sons: Claude (1906–1966) and Gabriel Paul (1910–1985). Claude worked in the travel business before joining NBC. He later served as eastern director for television of BMI, and at his death was executive director of the International Radio and Television Society. Gabriel, following in his mother's footsteps, became an actor. His theatre engagements included two seasons with the French Theatre of New York, in French. In 1937 he moved to Hollywood, where he appeared in more than 300 movies and played more than 1,000 television roles under the name Paul Bryar.

60. Brochure, Georges Barrère. 1919.

Nancy Toff, from the estate of Arthur Lora

The caption on the front cover of this brochure, issued by his manager, Catharine A. Bamman, terms him "The world's greatest virtuoso of the flute." The interior reprints in full an editorial by Dr. Frank Crane from the *New York Globe*. "Do you know who George Barrère is? Well, he is one of those persons who can do something better than anybody else in the world can do it." The back cover advertises his then-exclusive affiliation with the Columbia record label, listing solo, Barrère Ensemble, and Trio de Lutèce discs.

7

The Barrère Ensemble of Wind Instruments

61. A.W.K. "Unique Wood-Wind Organization Gives Final Chamber Music Concert." *Musical America,* **April 20, 1912, p. 35.**

NYPL

Charming pen-and-ink sketches by M.A. Stocking of the Barrère Ensemble and its leader illustrate this report of an ensemble concert at the Belasco Theatre on Sunday, April 14. The guest artist was pianist-composer André Caplet, conductor of the Boston Opera Company. Barrère and Caplet had been friends since their days in Paris in the late 1890s; together they had premiered Caplet's *Reverie* and *Petite Valse,* which Caplet wrote in 1897 and dedicated to Barrère. At this concert, they repeated these two short pieces by request, and were joined in Caplet's quintet for piano, flute, oboe, clarinet, and bassoon by oboist Bruno Labate, clarinetist Gustave Langenus, and bassoonist Ugo Savolini. The rest of the program was the Mozart *Serenade in E-flat,* Paul de Wailly's *Aubade,* and two movements from the *Suite, Op. 57* for woodwind quintet by Charles Lefebvre.

62. Photograph, The Barrère Ensemble of Wind Instruments.

Julia Drumm Denecke

63. Avery Strakosch. "Finds Public's Judgments Unreliable," *Musical America,* **May 29, 1915, p. 2.**

NYPL

The Barrère Ensemble made its first coast-to-coast tour in the spring of 1915. Barrère says of his colleagues: "It has been a sense of great satisfaction, a veritable joy to me, that my men find real pleasure in their work.... I never have to 'call' rehearsals. They ask for them, and will practice and rehearse without any limitation being placed upon their time. During our recent tour it was most amusing and gratifying to see them, on the long 'jumps' from one city to another take their instruments into the smoking car, and there, play for hours! It was a lovely feeling to know they were not merely mercenary musicians." The tour covered 13,000 miles, a first for such an ensemble of wind instruments. "It is very flattering to find how many ensembles have sprung into existence in the smaller cities, since our visits to them. Every week I receive letters inquiring for bits of music and advice. I am always happy to aid them in their kindly competition."

On the subject of programming, Barrère recalls that his first Ensemble program was straight classics—Bach, Beethoven, Handel, Haydn and Mozart;

only later did he program modern works. "Then I believed that the public really wanted us! You see, I never believe in the public's first judgment of an artist's work, or a creator's composition. Only after the public.... have had time to think over the artists and works, and then show a second judgment, do I believe them.

"Any modern composer will receive kindly attention from me. I do not believe in a personal individual criticism. If a modern is at all playable, he should be given a chance before the public. The public's decision, not mine or yours, is the thing that counts. The public may make a hasty decision at first, but it will always recognize its mistakes and acknowledge them, which is more than the average individual will do! One should never pay attention to the first, the direct criticism. Look back. You may see many examples of what I mean. Bizet's 'Carmen' and Wagner's 'Tristan' are proofs of the unfairness of sudden and hasty judgment."

64. Program, The Barrère Ensemble, George Barrère, conductor; Helen Stanley, soprano; Alberto Bimboni, piano. Cort Theatre, New York, December 19, [1916].

Charles Tomlinson Griffes scrapbook, NYPL

This program was a typical mix of the classic and the American, with songs interspersed. It began with the Mozart *Serenade in C minor* (wind octet) and continued with two movements from the *Quatuor for Four Flutes* by L. Kreutzer (played by Barrère, William Kincaid, Edward Meyer, and George Roscoe Possell). Next were two premieres: *The Vale of Dreams* and *The Lake at Evening,* two of three movements from Charles Tomlinson Griffes's *Three Tone-Pictures, Op. 5,* orchestrated by the composer for Barrère; and A. Walter Kramer's *Two Preludes (At Evening* and *An Oriental Sketch).* Next was Fritz Kreisler's *Caprice Viennois* ("Instrumentated by George Barrère. A bit of mild retaliation"). The program ended with five pieces by Chausson, *Nanny, Les Papillons, Sérénade italienne, Apaisement,* and *Le Cigale,* for soprano, wind ensemble, and piano.

In late 1915 Barrère had asked Griffes to write for his ensemble; the composer obliged with *The Lake at Evening,* which he transcribed from the piano original for flute, pairs of clarinets, oboes, bassoons, and horns, and harp. Barrère was evidently pleased with the result and asked him to transcribe the other two pieces of the *Tone-Pictures,* which Griffes did. (Some of the manuscript sketches are in the Griffes collection at the New York Public Library.) The third piece, *Night Winds,* apparently never appeared on a Barrère Ensemble program. Griffes re-arranged the three works for the New York Chamber Music Society, which premiered them in 1920.

In his autobiography, Barrère tells the story of the Kreisler piece: Barrère heard a benefit concert Kreisler gave in New York, at which the violinist played the "Dance of the Blessed Spirits" from Gluck's *Orpheus,* which Barrère refers to in his intentionally fractured English as one of his "battle horses." "I was slightly offended," Barrère wrote, "that he should play it to any flutist's detriment, so I went out before the end of the concert, bought the *Caprice Viennois,* and arranged it for my Ensemble."

65. Photograph, Barrère Ensemble [woodwind quintet], ca. 1932.

W. Stephen Thomas

Members of the quintet in the mid–1930s were (from left) Rudolph Puletz, horn; Angel Del Busto, bassoon; Carlos Mullenix,

oboe; Barrère; and Fred Van Amburgh, clarinet. In this photo, Van Amburgh holds a Haynes silver clarinet, a choice no doubt influenced by Barrère's association with Haynes. Van Amburgh's endorsement of the instrument, with its unique warming device, appeared in a full-page ad for the Haynes Co. in Barrère's autobiography.

66. Autographed program, Festival of Chamber Music, The Library of Congress, Washington, D.C., October 7, 1929.

Elizabeth Sprague Coolidge Collection, LC

The main attraction of this program was the first public performance of Joseph Hüttel's *Divertissement grotesque* for piano and woodwind quintet, which won the 1929 E. S. Coolidge Prize. The wind players also performed Franz Danzi's *Quintet in G, Op. 56, No. 2;* Barrère played the J.S. Bach *Sonata in E Major,* and Harold Bauer and Arthur Loesser played Bauer's two-piano arrangement of Beethoven's *Grand Fugue, Op. 134.*

65

The Trio de Lutèce

67. George Kossuth. Photograph, Trio de Lutèce, ca. 1914.

NYPL

Barrère, harpist Carlos Salzedo, and cellist Paul Kéfer had been friends since their student days at the Paris Conservatoire. Kéfer took first prize at the Conservatoire in 1900 and became a member of the Colonne and Lamoureux Orchestras and the Opéra-Comique in Paris. From 1908 to 1913 he was solo cellist of the New York Symphony. Salzedo, who won first prize in both piano and harp from the Conservatoire in 1901, was principal harpist of the Metropolitan Opera Orchestra from 1909 to 1913.

68. Trio de Lutèce. Announcement of concert, Belasco Theatre, [New York], February 22 (Washington's Birthday), [1914].

NYPL

This flyer announced the concert debut of the Trio de Lutèce, which took its name from Lutetia, the ancient Latin name of the members' former home, Paris. Guest artist for the concert was contralto Mme. Jeanne Gerville-Réache, "Prima Donna of the Montreal Opera Company."

69. Program, Trio de Lutèce, Belasco Theatre, [New York], February 22, 1914.

NYPL

67

In addition to solos for each of the three instrumentalists and two sets of songs, the program included a *Concert Royal* by François Couperin, Reynaldo Hahn's *Danses pour la Duchesse de Milan*, and Claude Debussy's *Petite Suite*. The cautious *New York Tribune* critic wrote (February 23, 1914), "There is probably a place for the trio in New York's musical life, though the circle which will enjoy the concerts is necessarily small."

THE BARRÈRE LITTLE SYMPHONY

Barrère's thirteen-member chamber orchestra began informally, as a pickup orchestra of New York Symphony members assembled for a benefit concert. From his earliest days as an orchestral musician, Barrère had worked with dancers (notably Isadora Duncan), and his own group often accompanied Duncan, her protégées such as Ruth Page and Anita Zahn, and Adolph Bolm's Ballet Intime. The symphony typically toured after the regular New York Symphony season ended. But after the demise of the New York Symphony, Barrère hoped to put his own orchestra on a more permanent basis—and so he formed committees, got endorsements from all the major New York critics, and appealed to such potential donors as Elizabeth Sprague Coolidge. He presented regular New York concert series and also toured extensively, drawing in later years on advanced students from Juilliard to join senior members of the orchestra.

Many of the concerts featured an eclectic combination of orchestral, chamber, and solo works, including sets by the Barrère Ensemble of Woodwind Instruments (generally the quintet version). "After the Concert" was an opportunity for solos and avant-garde works probably best not listed in the advertising. Barrère was zealous in his advocacy of contemporary composers in all idioms, premiering many works for chamber orchestra.

70. **Program. Concert for the Benefit of the New York Red Cross Hospital, 395 Central Park West, at 100th Street. Under the auspices of the Ladies' Auxiliaries and the Officers of the Hospital. Olive Fremstad, soprano; Carolyn Beebe, piano; The New York Little Symphony. Conductor, George Barrère, Flute. Carnegie Hall, [New York], February 27, 1914.**

Carnegie Hall Archives

This was the first performance of the group that would later be called the Barrère Little Symphony. The program consisted of *Pre-lude* by André Wormser, *Serenade et Valse, Op. 16, 17* by Vincent D'Indy, *Septuor in E flat, Op. 65* by Saint-Saëns, Wolf-Ferrari's *Kammersymphonie in B flat, Op. 8,* and various vocal numbers. Barrère recalled in his autobiography, "At the time I did not realize that this organization would be so successful"; he changed its name to avoid confusion with the New York Symphony.

71. **Brochure, Adolph Bolm Ballet Intime and the Little Symphony.**

Dance Collection, NYPL

72   73

72. Photograph, Georges Barrère with Russian Ballet billboard, San Francisco, 1921.

Dayton C. Miller Flute Collection, LC

Adolph Bolm came to the United States as leading artist and ballet master of Diaghilev's Ballet Russe, and remained here as a member of the Metropolitan Opera Company. His Ballet Intime, which he founded in 1916, presented an international array of dances, ranging from "the posturings of a Greek frieze in flat silhouette to a Russian revel, riotous of color and motion." The groups were brought together by Catherine Bamman, who managed both groups. In their joint programs, the orchestra performed in its own right and accompanied the dancers.

Merle Armitage, a young arts manager who helped manage their tours, recalled that "This made an ideal combination.... The pièce de resistance in my judgement, was Charles Griffes' *The White Peacock*." Of the tours, he wrote, "There was a great sense of cooperation in the company. There were no quarrels, there were no explosions. While travelling, orchestra men played poker with the ballet members, and loaned each other books and games. Harmony prevailed to a remarkable degree."

73. Flyer, Town Hall, New York, Friday, January 20 and Saturday, January 21, [1922].

Dance Collection, NYPL

This flyer announced the first performance of John Alden Carpenter's *Krazy Kat* ballet, as well as Szymanowski's *Ballet Grotesque to a comedy by Molière;* Poldowski's orchestral suite; and instrumental numbers by Carpenter, Poldowski, Szymanowski, and Prokofieff. The artists were Carpenter, Poldowski, Szymanowski, Adolph Bolm and his Ballet Intime, soprano Povla Frijsh, soprano Alice Miriam, and Barrère conducting his Little Symphony.

74. John Alden Carpenter. *Krazy Kat, A Jazz Pantomime. Based on the "Krazy Kat" newspaper cartoons of George Herriman. Arranged for piano by the composer.* **New York: G. Schirmer, 1922.**

NYPL

The piano score of *Krazy Kat* provides full credit for the Town Hall premiere: Music by John Alden Carpenter / Scenario by George Herriman / Staged by Adolph Bolm / Scenery and Costumes by George Herriman / Krazy Kat..Adolph Bolm / Officer Pup..Ulyssis Graham / Bill Postem..Ledra Stiffler / Joe Stork..Olin Howland / Ignatz Mouse..Bella Kelmans / Conductor, George Barrère / Costumes executed by Anne Neacy in the Russian Arts and Crafts Studio.

75. Flyer, Barrère Little Symphony, Booth Theater, [New York], March 18 and 25, 1928.

NYPL

The bill for the first concert, on March 18, was Gossec's *Symphony in G Major*; Quinto Maganini's *La Rumba* ("2nd time at these concerts. Request"); songs by Mozart Gretchaninoff, and Mussorgsky, sung by Nina Koshetz; Caplet's *Suite Persane;* and "After the Concert," the second New York performance of Edgard Varèse's *Offrandes.*

On March 25, Barrère scheduled Mozart's *Symphony No. 20, Three Pieces* by Chabrier, the Griffes *Poem* (with Kathleen Stewart at the piano), the world premiere of William Grant Still's *Log Cabin Ballads, Two Hungarian Dances* of Brahms, and "After the Concert," Debussy's unaccompanied *Syrinx* (listed as "new, first time") and Waldteufel's *Tout-Paris, Waltz.*

76. The Barrère Little Symphony. Season brochure, 1931-32. Concert Management Arthur Judson, New York.

Elizabeth Sprague Coolidge Collection, LC

This brochure contains extensive press quotes from 1930-31. A sampling: "A concert which must embarrass description by those weary of superlatives." (*Mail and Empire,* Toronto) "It was like an exhibit of French pastels. Barrère is a flutist extraordinary but he is a conductor who approaches perfection, too." (*Courier,* Evansville) "Barrère colors his talks with a fund of quaint wit that makes them almost as delightful as the music itself." (*Gazette,* Montreal) The featured quotation, from W. J. Henderson of the *New York Sun* (April 12, 1931), is, "Barrère is an unique and unreportable feature of his own concerts!"

77. Flyer, The Barrère Little Symphony, Town Hall, [New York], June 9, 1932.

NYPL

Barrère's New York concerts were his own enterprises, though his manager by this time was the Arthur Judson firm. This was one of a series of special concerts at "summer prices." After three orchestral works, Rossini's *L'Italiana in Algeri Overture,* Haydn's *Symphony No. 30 (The Schoolmaster),* and the "annual performance" of Chas. T. Griffes's *The White Peacock,* there was an *Intermède* by the Barrère Ensemble of Wind Instruments. This was actually the Barrère quintet (see catalog no. 65), which performed Ibert's *Trois pièces brèves* and three transcriptions by Barrère that were published in the *Juilliard Series of Music for Wind Instruments:* Delibes's *Petite Marche,* Strawinsky's [sic] *Pastorale,* and David Guion's *The Harmonica Player.* The orchestra program continued with Falla: *Four Popular Spanish Songs;* Debussy's *La Plus que Lente;* and Rameau's *Les Fêtes de l'Hymen et de l'Amour.* That was followed by the traditional "After the Concert," consisting of a mere two flute concertos, by Gretry and Vivaldi.

78. Barrère Little Symphony. Rehearsal and tour schedule, [spring 1939].

David Walter

79

There were two rehearsals scheduled at 30 West 56th Street (home of Barrère and the Beethoven Association) on February 19 and 21, in preparation for a February 22 departure. Nine concerts were scheduled in Illinois, Ohio, West Virginia, Massachusetts, Maine, New Jersey, Maryland, and Pennsylvania. Further instructions were: "Full dress, white vest, black socks & shoes for all night concerts. Cutaway suit, white shirt, black socks & shoes for all afternoon concerts. No music stand. Always bring sordino for all rehearsals and concerts."

79. Edward Treutel. Two tour photographs of Georges Barrère, 1938-39.

Edward Treutel

Edward Montrey, timpanist, is prominent in one of these photos, which were taken by trumpeter Edward Treutel. Surviving members of the Little Symphony recall great camaraderie on the tours, which were coordinated by Barrère and clarinetist/ manager Fred Van Amburgh.

80. Program, Barrère Little Symphony, ca. 1938-39.

David Walter

Many Little Symphony tours were under the auspices of the Civic Concert Service (also known as Community Concerts). One of the standard programs (there were generally two per tour) included Rossini's *L'Italiana in Algeri Overture,* Schubert's *Symphony No. 5,* Chas. T. Griffes's *The White Peacock* (which the Little Symphony performed more than 700 times, and which Barrère himself orchestrated for chamber orchestra), Gabriel Pierné's *For My Little Friends,* Debussy's *Menuet and Clair de Lune from "Suite Bergamasque,"* and *Three Pieces* by Isaac Albeniz. There were always flute solos at the end, but they were not on the printed program.

10

THE NEW YORK MUSICAL ESTABLISHMENT

81. Autographed photograph, Annual dinner meeting of the Beethoven Association and the 50th birthday of our president Harold Bauer. The Biltmore, [New York], April 28, 1923.

Harold Bauer Collection, LC

The photograph is signed by everyone in attendance, including Georges and Cécile Barrère (who is seated to the left of her husband). The guests included Jascha Heifetz, Franz Kneisel, Marcella Sembrich, Leopold Auer, Frank Damrosch, David and

81

Clara Mannes, Albert Stoessel, Herbert Witherspoon, Hugo Kortschak, Willem Willeke, Walter Golde, Sam Franko, Wilhelm Bachaus, René Pollain, Arthur Whiting, and Edouard Dethier.

82. Postcard, Beethoven Association. Second Concert—Tenth Season. Town Hall, [New York], November 19, 1928.

NYPL

For this all-Schubert program, Barrère played the *Introduction and Variations on an original theme, Op. 160* with pianist Rudolph Ganz, a collaboration arranged by Harold Bauer. The two had never previously played together. With Willy Meier-Pauselius, Hugo Kortschak, and Emmeran Stoeber, he performed the Quartet for flute, guitar, viola, and cello (1814; original manuscript found 1918, according to the Beethoven Association). Ernestine Schumann-Heink appeared on the program in a set of three songs.

83. Photograph, Beethoven Association concert, Town Hall, [New York], April 30, 1933.

NYPL

The program of this concert included a variety of vocal and instrumental ensembles and concluded with Saint-Saëns's *Carnival of the Animals*. The flutists were Barrère and Frances Blaisdell (front row), John Wummer and Frederick Wilkins (second row). Other participants were Richard Bonelli, Lucrezia Bori, Adamo Didur, Giuseppe Martinelli, Walter Damrosch, Harold Bauer, Ossip Gabrilowitsch, Josef and Rosina Lhevinne, Carlos Salzedo, Olga Samaroff, Ernest Schelling, and Albert Spalding.

84. Beethoven Association. Annual report, 1938/39.

NYPL

From 1925 to 1928 and 1930 to 1932 Barrère was an executive member at large of the Beethoven Association board. In 1932 he became a vice president and remained in that position until the organization disbanded in 1940; following founder Harold Bauer's resignation as president in 1939 he served as acting president.

85. Program, The Bohemians (New York Musicians' Club), December 27, 1924.

NYPL

Barrère served on the board of governors of The Bohemians from 1936 to 1940 and as vice president beginning in 1941. He appeared frequently on the programs of its private concerts. This particular program featured the American premiere of Barrère's *Symphony Digest,* "in honor of Walter Damrosch." The composer conducted. A clever pastiche, it conflates snatches of Beethoven's Fifth and Ninth Symphonies and Strauss's *Blue Danube Waltz* into the first several bars. Unfortunately, the score has been lost. Other works on the program, also American premieres and in manuscript, were: *Romeo and Juliet, Parody for Orchestra* by Moritz Kassmeyer (Vienna 1831–1884), directed by Franz Kneisel; *The Dead Basson (Der Todte Faggott), Fantastic Trio for tenor, basson [sic], and piano* by Karl Konradin (Vienna 1833–1844); and *The Nibelung's Ring, Paraphrased Valse for Orchestra, Paraphrased Valse for Orchestra* by Arthur Felkl, "under direction of a famous Guest Conductor," presumably the great Damrosch himself.

86. Flyer, Madison Square Garden, First Festival Concert. November 18, [1933]. Arranged and conducted by Walter Damrosch for the benefit of the Musicians Emergency Fund, Inc.

Walter Damrosch Collection, NYPL

Walter Damrosch served as chairman of the Musicians Emergency Fund and

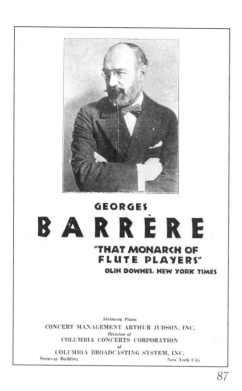

GEORGES

BARRÈRE

"THAT MONARCH OF FLUTE PLAYERS"

OLIN DOWNES, NEW YORK TIMES

Steinway Piano
CONCERT MANAGEMENT ARTHUR JUDSON, INC.
Division of
COLUMBIA CONCERTS CORPORATION
of
COLUMBIA BROADCASTING SYSTEM, INC.
Steinway Building   New York City

87

heights—it was as if Pan himself were calling."

88. Flyer. Carnegie Hall announces Twelve Lectures on Music with soloist and orchestra. Under the general direction of Olin Downes. [1940–41].

NYPL

Olin Downes, music critic of the *New York Times,* organized this Saturday-morning series by Juilliard faculty members and other leading New York musicians. Barrère gave his presentation on the woodwinds on February 8, 1941, with the assistance of Frances Blaisdell, flute; Annabel Hulme, piccolo; Carlos Mullenix, oboe; Lois Wann, English horn; Fred Van Amburgh and Alex Williams, clarinet; William Bortman, bass clarinet; and Louis Letellier and Angel Del Busto, bassoon. The lecture series was later published as *Be Your Own Music Critic,* edited by Robert E. Simon (Garden City, N.Y.: Doubleday, Doran, 1941).

organized a series of five concerts in 1933–34 for the benefit of needy musicians. This Bach-Wagner program included the Bach fourth Brandenburg concerto, with Albert Spalding, Barrère, and Frances Blaisdell as soloists.

87. Flyer. Georges Barrère, "That Monarch of Flute Players."

Hortense Barrère

This promotional flyer issued by Barrère's manager, Arthur Judson, takes its headline from Olin Downes of the *New York Times* and quotes superlatives from critics around the country. The *New York Sun* termed him a "magician of the flute," and the *Houston Post Dispatch* wrote, "There is but one Barrère." The *Los Angeles Herald* proclaimed, "Every inch an artist, this man; sound musicianship, refinement of feeling, taste, finesse, and intelligence were ever disclosed in his playing. Gluck's 'Orpheus' was music wafted from Olympian

88

11

ELIZABETH SPRAGUE COOLIDGE, PATRON

Barrère's first association with Elizabeth Sprague Coolidge, doyenne of American chamber music, was in the early 1920s. Over the years he played for many of her undertakings—at her Pittsfield, Massachusetts, estate; at the Library of Congress in Washington, D.C., where her foundation sponsored extensive chamber music festivals; at the Ojai Festival in California; and at numerous other events in the United States and Europe. In 1929, he even appealed to Mrs. Coolidge for support for his own enterprise, the Little Symphony, to which she did contribute from time to time. There is extensive correspondence between the two regarding programming and commissions of new music; though Barrère was not shy about expressing his opinions, he was almost obsequious in his attentions and deference to his patron.

89. Program, Barrère Ensemble of Wind Instruments, Berkshire Festival of Chamber Music, [September 30], 1921.

Barrère was a frequent artist at Mrs. Coolidge's chamber music festivals at her Pittsfield, Massachusetts, estate. At the fourth festival, Barrère's woodwind quintet (Barrère; Pierre Mathieu, oboe; Fred Van Amburgh, clarinet; Louis Letellier, bassoon; and Santiago Richart, horn), assisted by Alfredo Oswald, piano, played the Friday morning concert. Their repertoire was Mozart's *Quintet in E flat* for piano, oboe, clarinet, horn, and bassoon; Leo Sowerby's woodwind quintet; the Bach flute sonata in E major; the premiere of Domenico

Brescia's *Dithyrambic Suite* for woodwind quintet; Vincent d'Indy's *Sarabande and Menuet;* and Albert Roussel's *Divertissement* for piano and woodwind quintet (which had been written for the Société Moderne in 1906, the year after Barrère came to the United States).

90. Elizabeth Sprague Coolidge. Check to Georges Barrère, August 31, 1929, $1000. Check to Cécile Barrère, October 18, 1929, $500.

Elizabeth Sprague Coolidge Collection, LC

Mrs. Coolidge wrote a series of checks to the Barrères as payment for his October

woodwind quintet (Alfred Casella, piano; Barrère; and members of the Prague Woodwind Quintet). Barrère had played the world premiere of the Hüttel piece two weeks earlier (see catalog no. 66). The Roussel received its Paris premiere, again with Barrère, Tertis, and Kindler, on October 28, on a program that also included the first performance of Salzedo's *Préambule et Jeux,* which Barrère conducted.

92. Program, Programme of Chamber Music. Invitation Concert given by Mrs. Elizabeth Sprague Coolidge in the Hall of St. John's College, Cambridge, October 31, 1929.

Elizabeth Sprague Coolidge Collection, LC, and NYPL

This private concert included three works: Sir Arthur Bliss's *Quintet for Hautboy and Strings* (Léon Goossens and the Pro Arte Quartet), Martinů's string quintet, and Josef Hüttel's *Divertissement Grotesque* (with Barrère; Goossens; Albert Casella, piano; Haydn Draper, clarinet; Paul Draper, bassoon; and Edmund Chapman, horn).

93. Georges Barrère, New York. Telegram to Elizabeth Sprague Coolidge, Hotel Biltmore, Los Angeles, California, April 30, 1930.

Elizabeth Sprague Coolidge Collection, LC

Though the message is short— "ACCEPT EVERYTHING LETTER FOLLOWS GREETINGS"—it is indicative of Barrère's sensitive handling of his powerful patron. This particular telegram pertained to arrangements for a series of chamber music concerts to be held at the Field Museum in Chicago the following October. Barrère was to play the Roussel *Trio* and the Barrères were to be Mrs. Coolidge's guests at the Blackstone Hotel (though in February Barrère wired her that he would gladly play the Hüttel rather than Roussel). Over the three days of the festival, Barrère played the Hindemith *Sonatina in Canon Form, for Two Flutes, Op. 31, No. 3* (with his former

1930 concerts for her in Europe. The sites included Prague, Paris, and England.

91. Program, Koncert z děl Komorní Hudby složených z podnětu pí E. S. Coolidge [Concert of Chamber Music Composed by Commission of E. S. Coolidge], Palác "U Nováků," Prague, Rijna [October] 22, 1929.

Elizabeth Sprague Coolidge Collection, LC

The concert was organized under the patronage of His Excellency Mr. Lewis Einstein, Special Envoy and Minister Plenipotentiary of the United States of America to Prague, by the Association of Modern Music (Czechoslovakian section of the International Society of Contemporary Music). The main attraction was the world premiere of Albert Roussel's *Trio for flute, viola, and cello* (played by Barrère, Lionel Tertis, and Hans Kindler). Also on the program were Bohuslav Martinů's *Quintet for strings,* Alfredo Casella's *Sonata No. 2 in C* for cello and piano, and Josef Hüttel's *Divertissement Grotesque* for piano and student Ernest Liegl, then principal flutist of the Chicago Symphony), with the composer in attendance; Bach's *Sonata No. 6 in E Major* (with Emma Lübbecke-Job, piano); the American premiere of the Roussel trio (with Joseph Vieland, viola, and Iwan d'Archambeau, cello); a sonata by Mario Pilati; and Carlos Salzedo's *Préambule et Jeux*, a mixed chamber work conducted by the composer.

94. Program, Compositions of Paul Hindemith. Eighth Festival of Chamber Music, Library of Congress, Washington, D.C., April 10, 1937. Autographed by Barrère and Hindemith.

Elizabeth Sprague Coolidge Collection, LC

This all-Hindemith program, part of a three-day chamber music festival, included the world premiere of the 1936 flute sonata, with Jesús M. Sanromá at the piano. Hindemith made his first visit to the United States for this concert, where he performed his viola sonata. Francis D. Perkins wrote in the *New York Herald Tribune* (April 11, 1937): "The flute sonata, among the three works [the flute, viola, and piano sonatas], exhibited the most apparent degree of poetic musical speech, and was aided in doing so by the delectable tones of Mr. Barrere's flute." Henry Pleasants' review (April 17, 1937) was more positive: "This is a delightful composition, simple, melodious and punctuated with ingenious rhythmic devices. Mr. Barrère fairly outdid himself in displaying the solid merits of the piece as well as his own unique artistry as a flutist."

95. Autographed program, The Barrère Ensemble of Wind Instruments, Twentieth Anniversary of the Berkshire Festival of Chamber Music, South Mountain, Pittsfield, Mass., September 22, 1938.

Elizabeth Sprague Coolidge Collection, LC

On this occasion, Barrère played a Telemann sonata in C minor, Walter

Piston's *Three Pieces for flute, clarinet, and bassoon*, Nicolai Berezowsky's *Suite, Op. 11* for woodwind quintet (which was dedicated to Barrère), and Maurice Ravel's *Introduction and Allegro* for harp, flute, clarinet, and string quartet. Participating artists were members of the Barrère Ensemble of Wind Instruments (Fred Van Amburgh, clarinet; Carlos Mullenix, oboe; Rudolph Puletz, horn; and Angel Del Busto, bassoon); the Coolidge String Quartet (William Kroll and Nicolai Berezowsky, violins; Nicolas Moldavan, viola; Victor Gottlieb, cello); Sylvia Meyer, harp; and Jesús M. Sanromá, piano.

96. Georges Barrère. Typed letter, signed, to Elizabeth Sprague Coolidge, December 8, 1940.

Elizabeth Sprague Coolidge Collection, LC

Barrère accepts Mrs. Coolidge's invitation to the Colony Club in New York, an invitation apparently to perform as well as dine with Mrs. Coolidge. "It came to my mind that perhaps some music of Darius Milhaud would be played that evening and I come to offer you my collaboration, if you think it worth while in performing his Sonatine for flute and piano that he wrote in 1922.... I have played it very often and the public and musicians like it every time. I also suppose that your budget has been calculated; but in this occasion I would be much obliged if you would let me offer you this small contribution as a present. You have been so often so generous and thoughtful toward me, that it would give me a great and sincere joy to make it (let us say) a Christmas souvenir."

97. Program, Milhaud Program, Colony Club, New York, December 29, 1940.

Jerome Rappaport

Barrère and Jerome Rappaport played the *Sonatine*; Henri Temianka and the composer played several works for violin and piano; and Mme. Madeleine Milhaud recited two sets of poems.

12

BARRÈRE-SALZEDO-BRITT

In 1932, Barrère organized yet another flute, harp, and cello trio, the same instrumentation as the Trio de Lutèce; in fact, only the cellist changed, to Horace Britt. Barrère and Britt had met at the Paris Conservatoire when both were in their teens; they both graduated in July 1895 with first prizes, played together in the Concerts Colonne, and came to New York in 1905. Britt then played in the Letz and Elman Quartets and the Chicago, Minneapolis, Philadelphia, and San Francisco Symphonies. Barrère-Salzedo-Britt's programs generally included three works for the trio, and solo numbers for each member (Salzedo also served as harp or piano accompanist for his colleagues' solos.)

98. Carlos Salzedo. Autograph letter, signed, to Elizabeth Sprague Coolidge, June 28, 1933.

Elizabeth Sprague Coolidge Collection, LC

Salzedo reports to Mrs. Coolidge that "the BSB has achieved a most significant first season. Composers are positively wild over the unlimited musical resources of our instrumental combination! It reveals to them a new world of sound—opens unknown horizons. Already, we have [a] few works written for us by Wallingford Riegger, Aurelio Giorni, Bernard Wagenaar, and Evelyn Berckmann. Moreover, Ravel, Florent Schmitt, Honegger, Enesco, Casella, Ibert, Grainger, Tansman, Berezowsky, Cowell, Copland are interested in our group. This makes me think of an idea which I believe I suggested to you, that is, to have a composition contest for a chamber music work for Flute, Harp and Cello. I am confident that this novel type of chamber music would attract all composers most vividly." Mrs. Coolidge declined the offer to start such a contest, but she often invited the trio to perform at her concerts.

99. Flyer, Barrère-Salzedo-Britt. First Joint Recital in New York. Town Hall, Tuesday, May 8, 1934.

Wallingford Riegger Collection, NYPL

This handsome, two-color flyer announces not only the debut performance of the Barrère-Salzedo-Britt combination, but also the premiere of the trio for the same combination by the New York violinist Boris Koutzen (1901–1966). This was not, of course, the first time the three men had played together in New York, but the first time they had played a full joint recital in New York. The reviews of the Riegger

103

Divertissement were more critical than they had been at its premiere on December 11, 1933 (see catalog no. 40). The *New York World Telegram* (May 9, 1934) termed the concert "one of [the season's] most provocative events.... Three factors made the event memorable—the novelty and suitability of the instrumental combination, the fine musicianship of each of the artists, made evident in ensemble and in individual playing, and the tastefully assembled program, which juxtaposed, with an ear to contrast, such works as a flute sonata by Bach and the riotously modernistic 'Divertissement' by our own Wallingford Riegger."

100. Flyer, Barrère-Salzedo Britt in Unique Programs for Flute, Harp and Cello (interior).

Elizabeth Sprague Coolidge Collection, LC

Photographs and biographies of the three members are accompanied by choice press quotes. For Barrère: "That monarch of flute players" (Olin Downes, *New York Times*). For Salzedo: "The commanding figure of the harp world" (H. T. Parker, *Boston Transcript*). For Britt: "Hero of many musical triumphs in this country and abroad" (*San Francisco Call and Post*). The flyer's sample program includes Jean-Philippe Rameau's *Pièces en concert,* a set of three short pieces: Georges Valensin's *Menuet,* the Negro spiritual *Deep River,* and Jules Mouquet's *Dorienne;* and Ravel's *Sonatine en trio,* as arranged by Salzedo from the piano sonatina. Barrère's solo assignment was the Griffes *Poem* (with Salzedo at the piano).

101. Program, Barrère-Salzedo-Britt, Casimir Hall, The Curtis Institute of Music, November 25, 1936.

C. David McNaughton

The trio selections were Locatelli's *Trio Sonata,* Rameau's *Pièces en concert,* and Debussy's *Children's Corner* (transcribed by Salzedo from the *Piano Suite*). Barrère's solos were the *Air de Ballet from "Ascanio"* by Saint-Saëns (probably in Barrère's own arrangement, published by Galaxy), and Fauré's *Fantaisie.* Julius Baker, then a student at Curtis, remembers attending this recital, at which Barrère added a performance of Varèse's *Density 21.5* on his recently-acquired platinum flute (see catalog nos. 43–53).

102. Photograph, Barrère-Salzedo-Britt, Miami, Florida, *Musical Courier,* March 3, 1934, inside back cover.

NYPL

The trio donned appropriate headgear for a publicity photo while on tour in Miami.

103. Postcard photograph, Barrère-Salzedo-Britt, Butte, Montana, April 1935.

Elizabeth Sprague Coolidge Collection, LC

Outfitted in miners' helmets, the trio emerges from 2,800 feet underground in a Butte, Montana, copper mine. On tour, the trio signed and mailed this postcard to their patron, Elizabeth Sprague Coolidge.

13

THE BARRÈRE-BRITT CONCERTINO AND BARRÈRE TRIO

When Barrère-Salzedo-Britt disbanded, due in large part to the difficulties of transporting the harp, Barrère and Britt formed a quintet, the Barrère-Britt Concertino. Organized in 1937, the group also included violinist Mischa Elzon, pianist Jerome Rappaport, and a rotating roster of violists: Gerald Kunz, Frank Clawson, and William Carboni. The programs, as with the smaller group, employed the players in various combinations. At about the same time, Barrère, Britt, and Rappaport formed a trio that lasted until Barrère had his first stroke in 1941.

104. Flyer, The Barrère-Britt Concertino. ca. 1937-38.

Jerome Rappaport

The Concertino was billed in this brochure as "the last word in Chamber Music." It provided the following biographies: Mischa Elzon had been concertmaster of the Barrère Little Symphony for the past six years and had been assisting artist to soprano Ernestine Schumann-Heink. Gerald Kunz had studied with Franz Kneisel at the Institute of Musical Art and had taught for ten years at the Eastman School of Music, where he was a member of the Kilbourne String Quartet. He joined Barrère and Britt every summer at the Maverick Colony of Musicians in Woodstock, N.Y. Jerome Rappaport had studied at Juilliard with Ernest Hutcheson, Albert Stoessel, and Rubin Goldmark, and had been a soloist with the Barrère Little Symphony in 1924, when he was only fourteen. He had also spent two seasons as conductor of the San Antonio Symphony. The sample programs included a Telemann *Sonata a quattro in A,* the Beethoven *Serenade, Op. 25,* the Griffes *Poem,* a quintet by Rimsky-Korsakov, *Terzettino* for flute, violin, and viola by Henri Marteau, the Mozart flute quartet in A major, Chopin's *Nocturne and Valse* for flute and piano, and a final set for the full quintet: *La Plus Qui Lente* by Debussy, *Gopak* by Moussorgsky, and *La Jota Aragonese* by Saint-Saëns.

105

105. Advertisement, The Barrère-Britt Concertino. Season 1939-40. Concert Management Arthur Judson, Inc. Reprinted from *Musical America*, February 10, 1939.

Jerome Rappaport

Having completed 32 engagements in the U.S. and Canada between January 8 and March 7, the Concertino advertises itself as "equally successful in small towns and big cities." It is "An Unusual Concert Attraction" capable of "31 fascinating different instrumental combinations."

106. Program, Barrère-Britt Concertino, Sociedad Pro-Arte Musical [SPAM], Havana, Cuba, February 21, 1938.

Jerome Rappaport

This was the first of two concerts in Havana; the second was on Februrary 23. Other artists on the SPAM 1937–38 series were pianists Jose Iturbi and Harold Bauer, and singers Elisabeth Rethberg and Ezio Pinza, who appeared in two joint recitals. The program included Handel's *Concerto No. 1 in D minor* (flute, violin, cello, piano;

Beethoven's *Serenade in D Major, Op. 25* (flute, violin, viola); Fauré's *Fantaisie* (flute and piano); and a 1928 quintet by Jean Cras (1879–1932), a rear admiral in the French navy and the 1921 winner of the first prize of the City of Paris.

107. Two photographs, Barrère-Britt Concertino, Thomasville, Georgia, February 1940.

Jerome Rappaport

Bound for Atlanta by bus are Elzon, Rappaport, Britt, Barrère, and Carboni. In front of a palm tree in Thomasville, Georgia, the Concertino poses with two women from the local Community Concerts organization.

108. Flyer, The Barrère Trio. Concert Management Arthur Judson, Inc.

Carolyn Grant Morey

The flyer notes that the association of Barrère and Britt goes back "as far as they can remember, having met as "schoolboys at the Paris Conservatoire.... As for

51

Rappaport, Barrère claims to have brought him up! The pianist was still a prodigy when he appeared as soloist with the Barrère Little Symphony" in the Mozart D minor concerto. The *New York Herald Tribune* described Rappaport as "Among the most impressive of our younger pianists." Suggested repertoire includes trios by Haydn, Beethoven, Weber, Pierné, Goossens, and Riegger, and a variety of flute and cello sonatas.

109. Program, Georges Barrère, Flutist; Horace Britt, Cellist; Jerome Rappaport, Pianist. The Art Society of Pittsburgh, January 23, 1939.

Jerome Rappaport

The program included a trio sonata by Loeillet, Pierné's *Sonata da Camera, Op. 48*, the Hindemith flute sonata, and Weber's *Trio in G minor, Op. 73*. The Pierné, wrote the *Pittsburgh Press* critic, "is of virtuosic dimensions....The three musicians gave this work masterly projection, uncovered marvelous tonal qualities and surmounted the myriad technical difficulties with utmost ease." The Hindemith flute sonata, he continued, "bristles with dissonance throughout its three movements." But "for all its ultra modernism the manner in which Messrs. Barrère and Rappaport gave utterance to ... this sonata constituted a rare artistic feat that roused the audience to ovations of applause."

14

CHAUTAUQUA

Barrère's long association with the Chautauqua Institution in upstate New York dates back to the 1920s. From 1920 to 1928 the New York Symphony Orchestra was the resident orchestra; after its merger with the Philharmonic in 1928, many of the same players returned as members of the new Chautauqua Symphony. Barrère was a fixture of Chautauqua life, taking on many private flute pupils, playing first flute in the orchestra, and serving as assistant conductor (and in 1932 and 1936, acting conductor) of the orchestra. He also conducted a "Little Symphony" for several years.

110. *The Chautauquan 1936*. Brochure of the Chautauqua Institution.

Chautauqua Institution Archives

The brochure advertises "Everything you enjoy doing is found at Chautauqua New York." It states that although Chautauqua's musical director, Albert Stoessel, has arranged the entire summer's programs, he would take a leave of absence to complete an opera he was composing. Barrère took his place as conductor of the Chautauqua Symphony. The first week, the week of July 15, was devoted to the Little Symphony; the full orchestra would play 32 concerts between July 22 and August 22. Sunday afternoon concerts were broadcast over the NBC Blue Network, carried by some 40 stations.

111. Brochure. World's Greatest Flutist at Chautauqua, N.Y. Announcement concerning George Barrere and Detailed Music Programs, July-August, 1921. Chautauqua Institution, 1921.

Nancy Toff, from the estate of Arthur Lora

In 1921 Chautauqua welcomed Barrère to its summer school faculty. The brochure announced, "he will be available to a limited number of pupils for the six weeks beginning Monday, July 11th." It goes on to quote a *San Francisco Journal* review of his performance there the previous May: "We have few artists today who are the peers of George Barrère, Casals and Kreisler; these are probably the only two instrumentalists of our time who have the vision and the imaginative insight which rests in the music of this great master of the flute." The concert schedules at the back of the booklet list Barrère as flute soloist with the orchestra on three occasions.

112. *The Chautauqua Quarterly*, January 1921, p. 58.

Chautauqua Institution Archives

Barrère's fees for flute lessons, which were higher than those of other music teachers at the time, are listed as follows:

12 hour lessons	$70.00
10 hour lessons	$50.00
12 half hour lessons	$45.00
10 half hour lessons	$40.00
6 half hour lessons	$25.00

113. Photograph, Georges Barrère with student Ardelle Hookins, Athenaeum Hotel, Chautauqua, N.Y., July 1925.

Dayton C. Miller Flute Collection, LC

Ardelle Hookins, age twelve when this picture was taken, studied with Barrère at Chautauqua and, two years later, for ten weeks in New York. As a member of The Hookins Entertainers Deluxe with her father and brothers, she performed lunch and dinner music at the Athenaeum. Barrère insisted that she complete high school before entering the Institute of Musical Art, so she auditioned for William Kincaid at Curtis. She spent six years as the only woman in the Curtis wind department, graduating in 1934. Later she played in the Boston Women's Symphony under Ethel Leginska.

114. Panoramic photograph, Chautauqua Symphony Orchestra, 1937.

Samuel Coscia

Barrère is first flutist; Albert Stoessel is the conductor. The other flutists that year were Frederick Wilkins and Arthur Plettner. Mischa Mischakoff was the concertmaster.

113

115. Postcard. Chautauqua Symphony Orchestra Broadcasts on Sundays July 28, August 4–11–18 [1935].

Elizabeth Sprague Coolidge Collection, LC

The National Broadcasting Company, WEAF, and the Basic Red Network broadcast the Sunday concerts of the Chautauqua Symphony. This postcard announces the program for July 28, under conductor Albert Stoessel. Barrère was soloist in the Overture, Polonaise-Double, and Badinerie from Bach's *Suite in B minor*. This was his first public performance on his new platinum flute (see catalog nos. 43-53).

116. Photograph, dinner for the Chautauqua Symphony Orchestra and other musicians hosted by Georges and Cécile Barrère, Chautauqua, New York, August 16, 1936.

Samuel Coscia

119

During the summer of 1936, Stoessel was on leave and Barrère conducted the orchestra except for a one-week guest conducting stint by Howard Hanson. On August 16, he and Cécile (standing, rear center), who was renowned as a cook and hostess, gave this dinner party for the orchestra members and other musicians.

117. Photograph, Georges and Cécile Barrère, Hotel Athenaeum, Chautauqua, New York.

Chautauqua Institution Archives

The Barrères customarily lived at the stately Hotel Athenaeum, the major hotel on the grounds and just a short distance from the Amphitheater, where the symphony concerts were held. The photo is signed "A notre très chère amie, des ses deux bien devotées Cécile et Georges" in Cécile's hand.

118. Photograph, Georges and Jean Barrère, ca. 1924.

Dayton C. Miller Flute Collection, LC

Jean Clément Barrère (1918–1977) was the only child of Georges and Cécile Barrère. He was a noted theatre director and stage manager whose credits included *Life With Father, South Pacific, Sunrise at Campobello, The Pajama Game,* and *The Unsinkable Molly Brown.* He also directed shows in summer theatres around the country and in the early 1970s was in charge of productions at the Central City (Colorado) Opera House Association.

119. Samuel Goldman. Two photographs, Georges Barrère playing baseball. Chautauqua, New York, mid–1930s.

Samuel Goldman

The informal atmosphere at Chautauqua allowed time for picnics, county fairs, and baseball games—though Barrère retained his tie for the occasion.

120. Photograph, Georges Barrère and Dr. Arthur E. Bestor at a costume party, Chautauqua, New York.

Chautauqua Institution Archives

Costumed in a woman's hoop skirt and bonnet, Barrère accepts a basket from Arthur Bestor, the president of the Chautauqua Institution. At left is opera singer Warren Lee Terry.

15

THE MAVERICK, WOODSTOCK, NEW YORK

The Barrères spent many summers in rustic Woodstock, New York, where writer Hervey White had established The Maverick, an artists' colony. Barrère gave private lessons to New York students and to others, including some from the nearby summer camp of the Ernest Williams School of Music. (In the winter, he also took students from the Williams School, which was located in Brooklyn, New York.)

121

122

121. Photograph, Georges and Cécile Barrère at their house, Woodstock, New York.

Nancy Toff, from the estate of Arthur Lora

The Barrères built this house on Woodstock Road, just down from the homes of Horace Britt and Hervey White, the founder of the Maverick Colony, and the Maverick Concert Hall. Below the Barrères' house were those of Pierre Henrotte, concertmaster of the Metropolitan Opera Orchestra and music director of the Maverick Concerts, cellist Paul Kéfer, and conductor Leon Barzin.

122. Photograph, Georges Barrère outside his teaching cabin, Woodstock, New York, summer 1940.

Jean Klussman Morehead

Barrère gave lessons in this simple building behind his house. He corresponded at length with students to set up lesson times and make travel arrangements; often he drove them back and forth from town.

123. Photograph, four panels, Georges and Cécile Barrère, Woodstock, N.Y.

Frances Blaisdell

124. Photograph, Georges Barrère playing tennis, Woodstock, N.Y.

Frances Blaisdell

125. Program, American and French Music for Piano and Flute, Maverick Sunday Concerts, [Woodstock, N.Y.], June 15, 1930. Inez Carroll, piano; Georges Barrère, flute.

Wallingford Riegger Collection, NYPL

The program consisted of Parker Bailey's *Sonata,* Wallingford Riegger's *Suite for flute alone,* the Griffes *Poem,* Enesco's *Cantabile et Presto,* Wormser's *Madrigal,* Widor's *Scherzo,* and Fauré's *Fantaisie.* This was Barrère's second performance of the Riegger; he had premiered it at the League of Composers in New York on February 2, 1930.

16

THE NEW YORK FLUTE CLUB

126. State of New York. Office of the Secretary of State, Albany. Certificate of The New York Flute Club, Inc., December 31, 1920.

New York Flute Club Collection, NYPL

The first meeting of the New York Flute Club was held on December 5, 1920, at which time a board of directors was appointed. Barrère was President, Mrs. Eliot Henderson, 1st Vice-President; William Kincaid, 2nd Vice-President; Milton Wittgenstein, Recording Secretary; and Lamar Stringfield, Treasurer. The idea began when Barrère invited sixteen flutists to his home to play the Kuhlau *Grand Quartet,* four to a part. Once the flute club was formally organized, it began the custom of monthly Sunday concerts.

127. Georges Barrère. Letter to Emil Medicus, Asheville, N.C., December 27, 1921.

Dayton C. Miller Flute Collection, LC

Barrère reports to the editor of *The Flutist* magazine: "The New York Flute Club has been working very slow but we had a very interesting Meeting to-day of the Directors and the Entertainment and Membership Committees and steps are going to be taken to give a new impulse to our organization.

Personally I am so busy that I cannot even attend every Meetings. The experience so far shows how difficult it is to run a Flute Club in a large City such as New York. The difference of interest and point of view between amateurs and Professionals is almost alarming. The Amateur sees in the club mainly the Entertainments for which the Professionals are in demand. This is some time very interesting for a young and ambitious man but some others feel that they are giving more than they receive. Established Artists do not care to appear in such a way that they have the feeling of giving free public lessons. It might seems quite mercenary to you that such ideas could interfere with the welfare of a club of Flute Players, but I think it is the main difficulty. In a general way the professionals would like to see the activities of the Club directed in a more efficient and artistic way. Playing duets, then trios, then Quartetts for 2-3-4 flutes will never develop the true musical taste of the Masses. I even heard once a very brilliant Amateur saying that he considered that the Flute Quartett should have the same place than the String Quartett on the Musical World!!! I love too much my instrument to misguide its reputation by seconding such a fanatical utterance. Flute is a charming instrument but trying to boost it too far is a dangerous boomerang. We have a French saying about 'Qui n'entend qu'une Cloche n'entend qu'un son' that I can clumsily translate thus 'Who listens to only one Bell hears only one Tone.' As a Musician I should deny such a saying as whoever invented it forgot about the rich overtones of any Bell. But the originator of such a false proverb was right in his meaning, and flutists may think it over. Too much Flute is perhaps worse than not enough: first: for the musical education and taste of the flutists. Second: for the reputation of our instrument and its players outside of the Flute's Guild."

128. New York Flute Club, Incorporated. Membership brochure, [1934].

New York Flute Club Collection, NYPL, and Stephen Thomas

This booklet, "for lovers of music and the flute," was published December 9, 1934, according to notes kept by Dr. William S. Thomas, who was apparently in charge of

membership. Copies were distributed at a club concert and sent to Emil Stock of Carl Fischer, various individuals, and *Jacobs' Orchestra Monthly*. The brochure included a

NEW YORK

FLUTE CLUB

Incorporated

FOR LOVERS OF MUSIC AND THE FLUTE

THE
NEW YORK FLUTE CLUB

was founded in 1920 by Mr. Georges Barrère for the purpose of bringing together friends of music, particularly of flute music. Its members are professional and amateur flutists and music lovers. Monthly meetings of the Club are held on Sunday afternoons from October to May, inclusive. At each meeting there are flute solos and *ensembles* by amateur players who may wish to play, accompanied by the Club's Pianist. This portion of the program occupies the time from 3:30 o'clock to 4:30 after which there is an intermission of one-half hour. At five o'clock a concert given by professional musicians brings an hour or more of notable music to the members present and their guests.

128

sample program, that of December 17, 1933, at which the performers were Barrère, Frances Blaisdell, Fred Wilkins, and Victor Harris, flutes; Alice Nichols, piano; and Aurelio Giorni, pianist-composer. The opportunities offered by the club were listed as follows: "Attendance at monthly concerts during the season and association with other persons interested in music and the flute. Hearing the flute, other instruments and vocal artists and observation of technic and interpretation. Playing the flute in the presence of others during the amateur hour, accompanied by an outstanding pianiste[sic]. Musical information from experts; obtained by hearing music played and discussed. Learning of music desirable for purchase and how to avoid purchase of undesirable music. Opportunity of having music sent on approval. A discount on the price of music purchased. Assembling with other persons for playing *ensemble* music. Encouragement of artists and the art of music."

129. L. F. Grant. Two pencil sketches of Georges Barrère, New York Flute Club, 1935.

W. Stephen Thomas

These sketches by an amateur member of the New York Flute Club were given to another active member, Dr. William S. Thomas, who kept them in his *Flute Scrapbook.* One appears on the cover of this catalog.

130. Program, The New York Flute Club, Incorporated. The Art Center, [New York], December 16, 1923. Recital of music for flute, edited or composed by Georges Barrère.

Charles Tomlinson Griffes scrapbook, NYPL

Barrère was assisted by flutist-pianist Kathlyn Woolf and flutist Sarah Possell, both his students. He began with a "Lecture with illustrations on the 26 studies" of Altès, and then performed the Griffes *Poem,*

Gluck's *Scene from Orpheus,* Mozart's *Menuet,* and his own *Two pieces for three flutes* and *Nocturne.* The trio was published by Carl Fischer; all the other works were published by G. Schirmer.

131. Program, The New York Flute Club, Incorporated. Recital of New Music for Flute. Beethoven Association Clubhouse, New York, December 18, 1938.

New York Flute Club Collection, NYPL

Barrère was assisted by pianists Alice Nichols, Richard Franko Goldman, and Jerome Rappaport. On the program were the *Sonatine* by Philippe Gaubert (dedicated to Barrère, new, first time), Marion Bauer's *Five Greek Lyrics* for flute alone (also dedicated to Barrère, new, first time), Yoritsune Matsudaira's *Sonatine,* Eugene Goossens's *Three Pictures* (dedicated to Ary Van Leeuwen, new, first time in New York), and Richard Franko Goldman's *Divertimento* (new, first time). Goldman was pianist in his own piece.

132. Program, The New York Flute Club, Incorporated. Recital of Flute Quartettes. Midtown Music Hall, New York, February 23, 1941.

New York Flute Club Collection, NYPL

Barrère was assisted here by eight students: Frances Blaisdell, Ruth Freeman, Carolyn Grant, Annabel Hulme, Mary Elizabeth Miles, Patricia Powell, David De Vol, and George Neitzert. The program consisted of Luigi Gianella's *Quartetto in G, Op. 52,* Frederick Kuhlau's *Grand Quatuor, Op. 103,* Robert Russell Bennett's *Rondo Capriccioso* (published by the New York Flute Club), Ary van Leeuwen's *Turkey in the Straw,* and Anton Reicha's *Quartett, Op. 12.*
For many years it was the custom of the New York Flute Club to present the Kuhlau quartet, which had been played at its first meeting in 1920, with multiple players on a stand.

17

JUILLIARD AND STUDENTS

133. Wm. S. Haynes Company. Boehm Flutes and Piccolos of Modern Construction [catalog]. Boston, 1925.

Ruth Cubbage Dorsey

A major portion of the Haynes Company's 1925 catalog was devoted to photographs of flutists who played the company's flutes. Many of the students are grouped with their teachers. On the Barrère page are R. Meredith Willson, Raymond E. Williams, Arthur Lora, E[dward] Meyer, George R. Possell (who played with his teacher in the New York Symphony), Mary Henderson, Kathlyn Woolf, Sarah Possell, Christine Howells Pfund, and Jeannette Rogers. William Kincaid, surrounded by his own students, already merited his own page.

134. Georges Barrère. Letter to [Dean Ernest Hutcheson], Juilliard School, March 25, 1931.

The Juilliard School Archives

This is Barrère's proposal for a woodwind ensemble program at Juilliard. He laments that "no experienced Musician expects from any wind Instrument player not even 50% of the Musical equipment required from a first class Violinist or Cellist....The repertoire for these Instruments is more extended than generally believed, but is pitifully neglected by Teachers, Students, and Schools.... What is true of the indi-

vidual repertoire is equally true of the Ensemble list. While forcibly much smaller than the wealthy repertoire of the String quartet, there are many compositions which should be known by every instrumentalist. This list could be easily augmented by careful transcriptions of classic works...."

Barrère notes that compared to string players, wind players in orchestras have "a proportional[ly] limited chance to be heard, criticized and advised." In view of increasing interest in wind instruments "even in High Schools," he recommends the following: cataloging of the best teaching material and ensemble music for wind instruments; establishment of ensemble classes for winds alone; and orchestral sectional classes "led by a leader who understands wind instruments thoroughly...."

135. Juilliard School of Music, New York City. Agreement between the Juilliard School of Music and Georges Barrère, May 1, 1931.

The Juilliard School Archives

Barrère had taught at the Institute of Musical Art since its first year, 1905–6. The IMA merged with the Juilliard Graduate School in 1926 to form the Juilliard School of Music, and Barrère joined the Juilliard faculty in 1931. There, in addition to teaching class lessons to graduate flute students, he founded the school's woodwind ensemble class. This contract covers the school year from September 28, 1931, to May 14, 1932, and obligates Barrère to give two hours of class instruction in wind instruments for 28 weeks. For this service he was to be paid $1,400, payable in eight monthly installments of $175.

136. Photograph, Juilliard Graduate School faculty, March 1936.

The Juilliard School Archives

Seated (left to right) are Madeleine Marshall, Alexander Siloti, Florence Page Kimball, Anna Schoen-René, Dean Ernest Hutcheson, Olga Samaroff Stokowski, Rosina Lhevinne, Albert Spalding, and Edith Braun. Standing, first row, are Paul Reimers, Louis Persinger, James Friskin, Josef Lhevinne, Edouard Dethier, Harold Hutcheson, Horatio Connell, René Vaillant, Peter Riccio, and Frederick Kiesler. Standing, second row, are Carl Friedberg, Francis Rogers, Felix Salmond, Oscar Wagner, Frederick Jacobi, Hans Letz, and Barrère. Standing, third row, are Albert Stoessel, Bernard Wagenaar, Arthur Mahoney, Alfredo Valenti, and Alberto Bimboni. Barrère performed with many of his Juilliard colleagues both in New York and at Chautauqua.

137. Program. Concert by Students in the Wind Ensemble Classes of Georges Barrère. Recital Hall, Juilliard School of Music, New York, April 29, 1941.

C. David McNaughton

Barrère's wind ensemble classes were mainly reading sessions; the groups only rarely performed publicly. The program of this Tuesday afternoon concert consisted of the Mozart *Serenade in C minor, K. 388*, Florent Schmitt's *Lied and Scherzo, Op. 54*, for double quintet of wind instruments, and Richard Strauss's *Suite in B flat* for double woodwind quintet and tuba, played from manuscript.

The 1932–33 ensemble class—which often tried out Barrère's woodwind quintet arrangements in manuscript—included Sol Schoenbach, future principal bassoonist of the Philadelphia Orchestra, and Leonard Sharrow, future principal bassoonist of the NBC and Pittsburgh Symphonies.

138. Photograph, William M. Kincaid, ca. 1920.

Dayton C. Miller Flute Collection, LC

139. Transcript, William Morris Kincaid, Institute of Musical Art, 1911–1920.

The Juilliard School Archives

Kincaid was Barrère's first star pupil. He played with his teacher in the New York Symphony (1913–19), filling in for Barrère as principal flute when Barrère did not tour (and during the 1918–19 season, which he took off). Kincaid also played in the New York Chamber Music Society (1919–21) before winning the principal chair in the Philadelphia Orchestra in 1921. In a letter to Emil Medicus, Barrère wrote, "I suppose you know that my pupil Wm. M. Kincaid has been engaged as first flute with the Philadelphia Orchestra—We, of N.Y., are very sorry to loose [sic] such a good friend; but I, his teacher, am very proud of his promotion."

140. Photograph, Arthur Lora and Arturo Toscanini, Sun Valley, Idaho, 1950.

Nancy Toff, from the estate of Arthur Lora

141. Photograph, Arthur Lora in his Juilliard studio.

Nancy Toff, from the estate of Arthur Lora

Arthur Lora (1903–1992) studied with Barrère from 1919 to 1924. In September 1925 he was appointed Barrère's assistant. He succeeded Barrère as the principal flute professor in 1944 and served on the faculty a total of 53 years. He also taught at the

140

Manhattan School of Music and the Montreal Conservatoire. Lora was first flutist of the City Symphony of New York (1922–23), the State Symphony of New York (1924–25), the Metropolitan Opera (1937–45), and the NBC Symphony under Toscanini (1947–52). As Barrère's successor at Juilliard, it was appropriate that his teacher's portrait adorned his studio wall.

142. Walter Damrosch. Letter to Georges Barrère, June 3, 1933; Georges Barrère. Letter to Walter Damrosch, June 7, 1933.

Walter Damrosch Collection, NYPL

Damrosch wrote to Barrère, "Last night I attended the commencement exercises of the Institute and heard your pupil play the Mozart concerto. It was beautiful and it makes me happy to think I happened to have been instrumental in bringing you to America. Quite apart from your individual contribution as a great musician, you have done so much in educating first class artists on your instrument." Barrère replied, "I am glad you liked Frances Blaisdell's playing. She is a good worker and has developed into a charming artist. Thank you for your kind congratulations on her behalf; but as I told her a few days ago, I don't think that

teachers make any more good students than students make good Teachers."

143. Flyer, Frances Blaisdell.

Frances Blaisdell

Frances Blaisdell auditioned for Barrère in 1928 and became the first woman wind player at the Institute of Musical Art; she studied with Barrère until 1934. She made her solo debut with the New York Philharmonic in 1932, the first woman wind player to solo with that organization. Blaisdell was accompanist to Lily Pons in concerts and recordings and was principal flute of the New Opera Company and the New Friends of Music. She formed the Blaisdell Woodwind Quintet (with four members of the New York Philharmonic) and toured with the Barrère Trio after Barrère had his stroke in 1941. For fifteen years she was principal flutist of the New York City Ballet Orchestra. Frances Blaisdell taught at the Manhattan School of Music, New York University, and the Dalcroze School, and, since 1973, has taught at Stanford University.

FRANCES BLAISDELL

FLUTIST

143

144. Flyer, New York Chamber Music Society, January 15, 1928. Meredith Willson, flute.

NYPL

Meredith Willson (1902–1984), one of Barrère's early students at the IMA (1920–21), is also pictured in the Haynes catalog group of Barrère students (catalog no. 133). He relates some of his adventures while studying with Barrère in his autobiography, *And There I Stood With My Piccolo*. Willson was principal flutist in the Sousa Band (1921–23) and a member of the New York Chamber Music Society and New York Philharmonic (1924–29), while continuing to study privately with Barrère. He achieved his greatest fame as composer of *The Music Man*.

145. Flyer, Lamar Stringfield.

Dayton C. Miller Flute Collection, LC

Lamar Stringfield (1897–1959) studied with Barrère at the Institute of Musical Art from 1920 to 1924. He later recalled, "I played the 'Poem' for flute and orchestra by Charles T. Griffes on my artist's program at the Institute of Musical Art…. That was the first time an American work had been played on an artist's program—thanks to the help of Mr. Barrère who backed my desire to play an American composer's work." Stringfield was flutist of the Chamber Music Art Society of New York and the New York Chamber Music Society and was involved in the flute making and repair business for some years. A number of Stringfield's compositions were performed at the New York Flute Club and on Barrère Little Symphony programs; his suite *From the Southern Mountains* won the Pulitzer Prize in 1928. In 1932 he founded the institute of folk music at the University of North Carolina and later the North Carolina State Symphony Orchestra.

146. Photograph, John H. Kiburz, Sr.

Dayton C. Miller Flute Collection, LC

John Kiburz, Sr., began his tenure with the St. Louis Symphony in 1899 as piccoloist. During 1910–11 he was in New York, where he studied privately with Barrère. He then turned down offers from the New York Symphony, New York Philharmonic, Metropolitan Opera House, Cincinnati Symphony, and Sousa Band and returned to St. Louis to take the principal flute chair. His son, John, Jr., followed him to Barrère, studying with him at the IMA from 1933 to 1936. He too returned to St. Louis, where he played piccolo in the Symphony.

147. Flyer, Maganini Chamber Symphony, Quinto Maganini, conductor. Town Hall, New York, November 26, 1933.

NYPL

Quinto Maganini (1897–1974) studied flute privately with Barrère and later studied composition with Nadia Boulanger in France. As a flutist he performed in the San Francisco Symphony (1917–19) and the New York Symphony (1919–28), where he played second to his teacher. Maganini was later active as a conductor, both of the Maganini Chamber Symphony (founded 1932) and the Norwalk (Conn.) Symphony, which he conducted for 30 years.

148. Photograph, Harry Moskovitz, 1932.

Dayton C. Miller Flute Collection, LC

Harry Moskovitz (1904–1981), a graduate of the New England Conservatory under Georges Laurent, studied with Barrère at Juilliard in 1932 and was a member of the NBC Symphony, CBS Symphony, St. Louis Symphony, New York City Center Symphony and Opera Orchestras, the Voice of Firestone Orchestra, and New York Philharmonic Stadium Concerts, and solo flute of the Goldman Band and Bell Telephone Hour. Moskovitz was president of the New

York Flute Club from 1957 to 1960 and 1967 to 1970.

149. Photograph, Frederick Wilkins.

Frances Blaisdell

Frederick Wilkins studied with Barrère at the Juilliard Graduate School from 1932 to 1936; his other teachers included Meredith Willson, also a Barrère student. He was solo flutist of the "Voice of Firestone" and taught at Juilliard, the Manhattan School of Music, and Teachers College. Wilkins played with Barrère in the Chautauqua Symphony, succeeded him as flute teacher there, and played the Gluck "Orpheus" at the unveiling of Barrère's bust there in 1952 (see catalog no. 155). Frederick Wilkins served as president of the New York Flute Club from 1955 to 1957.

150. Photograph, James B. Hosmer.

James B. Hosmer

James Hosmer studied with Barrère at the Juilliard Graduate School from 1934 to 1937, after three years' study with William Kincaid. He was first flute of the Indianapolis Symphony (1937–42) and the Worcester (Mass.) Festival Orchestra (1939–41) and a member of the Chautauqua Symphony Orchestra (1938–41, 1952–65), the New York Philharmonic Lewisohn Stadium orchestra (1947), and the Metropolitan Opera Orchestra (1946–76). His published compositions include a *Fugue in C* for woodwind quintet, *Rhapsody* for flute and strings, and *Four Flute Duos*. James Hosmer served for many years as financial secretary of the New York Flute Club.

151. Flyer, Ruth Freeman, Town Hall recital, New York, November 8, 1946.

NYPL

Ruth Freeman studied with Barrère for fourteen years, both at Chautauqua and at the Juilliard Graduate School (1936–40). She was for many years principal flute of the Musica Aeterna Orchestra in New York and also played in the Chautauqua and New York City Symphonies, at Radio City Music Hall, and in recital with the Salzedo Concert Ensemble and the New York Concert Trio. She taught in the Juilliard Preparatory Division.

152. Photograph, Samuel Baron.

Samuel Baron

Samuel Baron studied at Juilliard with both Barrère and Arthur Lora. He was a founding member of the New York Woodwind Quintet, of which he is still a member. In 1965 he became flute soloist of the Bach Aria Group and in 1980 assumed the musical directorship of the ensemble. Samuel Baron has premiered the works of such composers as Ezra Laderman, Alan Hovhaness, Pierre Boulez, George Perle, and André Jolivet, and has appeared at many summer festivals, including Norfolk, Music Mountain, Santa Fe, and Banff. He is flute professor and chair of the woodwind department at the Juilliard School and professor of music at the State University of New York at Stony Brook.

153. Photograph, Bernard Goldberg.

Bernard Goldberg

Bernard Goldberg began his flute studies with John Kiburz, Sr. (a Barrère student) and Laurent Torno and studied with Barrère from 1940 to 1943. He joined the Cleveland Orchestra in 1943 and became principal flutist two years later. From 1947 to 1993 he was principal flutist of the Pittsburgh Symphony. Bernard Goldberg has premiered works by Frank Martin, Virgil Thomson, Lennox Berkeley, John Williams, Leonard Bernstein, and Joseph Schwantner. He has taught at Carnegie-Mellon University and is on the faculty of the Brooklyn College Conservatory.

18

IMAGES OF BARRÈRE

154. Rudy F. Hermann. Pastel portrait of Georges Barrère. 1960.

The New York Flute Club

This portrait was originally owned by Jack Fulton, a former pupil of Barrère, who gave it to his friend Jack Linx. For many years the drawing hung in the Linx and Long music store on 48th Street in New York.

155. Marion Sanford. Bronze bust of Georges Barrère. 1934.

Wm. S. Haynes Co.

As a child vacationing at Chautauqua, Marion Sanford had idolized Barrère; when she became a sculptor she asked him to sit for his portrait, and he carefully showed her the proper hand position for flute playing. Two castings were made: the first (which is in this exhibit) is owned by the Wm. S. Haynes Co. of Boston. The second (pictured below) is at the Smith Memorial Library of the Chautauqua Institution, the gift of an anonymous donor in 1952. Marion Sanford held Guggenheim fellowships from 1941 to 1943 and won many other major prizes for her work.

155

160

156. Music stand formerly owned by Georges Barrère.

Harold M. Jones

This carved wooden music stand was immortalized in the 1915 sketch of Barrère that decorated his Barrère Ensemble and Little Symphony programs for many years. The sketch has also been used as a graphic device by the New York Flute Club.

157. Georges Barrère. *Deux pièces brèves pour trois flûtes.* New York: Carl Fischer, 1926.

Carl Fischer, Inc.

This is Barrère's only published piece for a flute ensemble. The two movements are "Preludiettino" and "Verlainade."

158. Photograph, Trio de Lutèce, Bar Harbor, Maine, ca. 1917–18.

George Koutzen

Barrère, Salzedo, and Kéfer, along with many New York musicians, spent summers during the World War I era in Seal Harbor, Maine. This photograph was taken at the Fine Arts Building in Bar Harbor. A similar photo, in the same setting, includes Harold Bauer, Ossip Gabrilowitsch, and Margaret Matzenauer. Out of this group grew the Beethoven Association, originally established to combat opposition to German music.

159. George Kossuth. Photograph, Georges Barrère, ca. 1921.

Bernard Goldberg

160. Photograph, Georges Barrère and Inez Carroll, Woodstock, New York.

Hortense Barrère

Barrère and Carroll frequently collaborated in concerts at Woodstock (see catalog no. 125).

161. Photograph, Georges Barrère with platinum flute, 1935.

Julia Drumm Denecke

162. Photograph, Georges Barrère and Marek Windhelm, December 30, 1935.

NYPL

The occasion for this photograph is not known, but tenor Marek Windhelm was a fellow member of the Beethoven Association who sang at the Metropolitan Opera in the 1920s and '30s.

163

163. Photograph, Georges Barrère, ca. 1938.

Nancy Toff, from the estate of Arthur Lora

164. Giulio Harnisch. Caricature of Georges Barrère.

Hortense Barrère

Giulio Harnisch was a violist in the New York Symphony and the Barrère Little

Symphony. Like Enrico Caruso, he was an excellent cartoonist and made a number of caricatures of Barrère. This one has never been published.

165. Frederick Zimmermann. Caricature of Georges Barrère. Signed by Barrère, May 1930.

Frances Blaisdell

166. Frederick Zimmermann. Caricature of Georges Barrère.

David Walter

Frederick Zimmermann, longtime member of the New York Philharmonic, also played double bass in the Barrère Little Symphony and taught at Juilliard.

167. Gold pocket watch with flute fob, owned by Georges Barrère.

Paul Barrère

168. Harry Moskovitz. Briar pipe head of Barrère.

Paula Moskovitz Easton

Harry Moskovitz, a Barrère student and president of the New York Flute Club (see catalog no. 148), was also an expert woodcarver. His subjects included Arturo Toscanini, who insisted on keeping Moskovitz's image of him.

169. Record album, J.S. Bach: *Sonatas*. Georges Barrère, flute; Yella Pessl, harpsichord. Victor Set M-406. 1937.

Ruth Cubbage Dorsey

This four-record set was recorded in June 1937 and issued the following December. It contains the *Sonata in B Minor, BWV 1030*; the *Sonata in E-flat Major, BWV 1031*; and the *Sonata in C Major, BWV 1033*.

170. Record album, Claude Debussy: *Children's Corner Suite,* **transcribed by Carlos Salzedo. Georges Barrère, flute; Carlos Salzedo, harp; Horace Britt, cello. Victor Set M-639. 1937.**

Hortense Barrère

This Salzedo arrangement was a staple of Trio de Lutèce and Barrère-Salzedo-Britt concerts. Its movements are *Dr. Gradus ad Parnassum, Jimbo's Lullaby, Serenade for the Doll, The Snow is Dancing, The Little Shepherd,* and *Golliwog's Cakewalk.* The recordings were made in May 1937 and issued in the spring of 1940.

171. Record album, Music of Bali. Arranged by Colin McPhee. Georges Barrère, flute; Benjamin Britten, piano; Colin McPhee, piano. Schirmer's Library of Recorded Music, Set No. 17. 1941.

Rodgers and Hammerstein Archives of Recorded Sound, NYPL

Colin McPhee transcribed two Balinese flute melodies for modern flute and piano, "Lagu ardja" (Ardja melody, arranged 1936) and "Kambing slem" (Black goat, arranged 1935). This recording was made and released in the spring of 1941. McPhee had appeared with the Barrère Little Symphony on March 23, 1930, playing his concerto for piano and wind octet.

172. Charlotte S. Morris. *Favorite Recipes of Famous Musicians.* **New York: Prentice-Hall, Inc., 1941.**

Hortense Barrère

To this anthology of recipes by and for musicians (mostly by singers and members of the New York Philharmonic), Barrère contributed "My Macaroni au Gratin." Bemoaning the lot of the traveling musician, consigned to hotel food that changes little from one town to another, he says that his wife [Cécile Barrère was known as a marvelous cook and hostess] "always manages to greet me back home with my

164

favorite Dish. That is a humble MACARONI *au GRATIN*. This is a French Dish, not an Italian one. Macaroni in France is very well made, and for the *au Gratin* proposition I think the name is widely abused in this Country. A *gratin,* to my French mind, cannot be made with anything else but the purest and most genuine Swiss cheese. I have been often accused by my Family or Friends who have partaken my table, of indulging in Cheese with Macaroni, rather than Macaroni with Cheese." Barrère follows his recipe with the comment, "It is so simple that I think some day I shall try to cook it myself! However, I shall be sure to have no Guest that day." The suggested menu consists of Alligator Pears [avocados] Vinaigrette; Fresh Asparagus, Sauce Hollandaise; *Poulet Grillé* (with French fried potatoes), My Macaroni *au Gratin,* A Green salad (perhaps), International assortment of cheeses; Fraises au Vin (or Kirchwasser), Demitasse; and various wines. It comes with a "Notice: Such menu is not especially recommended before the performance of a Concert!"

CHRONOLOGY

October 31, 1876	Born in Bordeaux, France
1889-96	Studies at Paris Conservatoire with Henri Altès (1889-93) and Paul Taffanel (1893-96); awarded *premier prix* July 29, 1895
December 23, 1894	1st flute in premiere of Debussy's *Prélude à l'Après-midi d'un faune*
1895	Founds Société Moderne d'Instruments à Vent
1897-1905	Member of Colonne Orchestra: 3rd flute to 1903, then 1st flute
1899-1905	Teaches at Schola Cantorum, Paris
1900-1905	4th flute in Paris Opéra
1903	Elected Officier de l'Académie Français
May 1905	Arrives in New York, May 13; solo debut with New York Symphony/ Damrosch, May 20
1905-28	1st flute, New York Symphony Orchestra/Damrosch
1905-30	Teaches at Institute of Musical Art
1910	Founds Barrère Ensemble of Wind Instruments
1913	Forms Trio de Lutèce with Paul Kéfer, cello; Carlos Salzedo, harp
February 2, 1914	Premieres Seth Bingham's *Suite for winds, Op. 17;* Mabel Wood Hill's *Two Pieces;* Florent Schmitt's *Lied and Scherzo, Op. 54* (Barrère Ensemble, N.Y.)
February 27, 1914	First concert of Barrère Little Symphony (then called New York Little Symphony)
1916	Divorced from Michelette Burani
December 19, 1916	Premiere of Charles Griffes's *The Vale of Dreams, The Lake at Evening;* A. Walter Kramer's *Two Preludes* (Barrère Ensemble, N.Y.)
July 6, 1917	Marries Cécile Elise Allombert
1918-19	Takes leave of absence from New York Symphony
November 16, 1919	Premieres Griffes *Poem* (New York Symphony/Damrosch)
February 13, 1920	Premieres John Beach's *Naive Landscapes;* N.Y. premiere of Gabriel Pierné's *Preludio e Fughetta, Op. 40, No. 1* (Barrère Ensemble)
December 11, 1920	Premieres David Stanley Smith's *Fête galante* (New York Symphony/ Damrosch)
December 1920	Founds New York Flute Club; elected president (serves to 1944)
1921	Becomes head of new flute department at Chautauqua Institution
January 20, 1922	Conducts premiere of John Alden Carpenter's *Krazy Kat* ballet (Barrère Little Symphony and Ballet Intime, N.Y.)
1923	Named Officier de l'Instruction Publique by French government

December 27, 1924	Premiere of Barrère's *Symphony Digest* (The Bohemians, Barrère conducting, N.Y.)
January 17, 1926	N.Y. premiere, Jacques Ibert's *Jeux* and Phillip Jarnach's *Sonatine* (with Lewis Richards, piano)
January 24, 1926	N.Y. premiere, Darius Milhaud's *Sonatine* (with Lewis Richards, piano)
January 31, 1926	N.Y. premiere, Albert Roussel's *Four pieces for flute and piano* (with Lewis Richards, piano)
February 24, 1927	Purchases Haynes gold flute
March 20, 1927	Premieres William Grant Still's *From the Black Belt* (Barrère Little Symphony, N.Y.)
March 25, 1928	Premieres William Grant Still's *Log Cabin Ballads* (Barrère Little Symphony, N.Y.)
October 22, 1929	Premieres Albert Roussel's *Trio for flute, viola, and cello* (with Lionel Tertis and Hans Kindler, Prague)
February 2, 1930	Premieres Wallingford Riegger's *Suite for solo flute* (League of Composers, N.Y.)
March 23, 1930	Premieres Mary Howe's *Sand, Mists;* U.S. premiere, Heitor Villa-Lobos's *Choros No. 2* (Barrère Little Symphony, N.Y.)
February 9, 1931	Becomes U.S. citizen
June 3, 1931	Premieres Mabel Wheeler Daniels's *Deep Forest* (Barrère Little Symphony, N.Y.)
1931-44	Teaches at The Juilliard School
1932	Forms Barrère-Salzedo-Britt
Summers 1932, 1936	Acting conductor of Chautauqua Symphony Orchestra
Summer 1933	Founds Chautauqua Little Symphony
December 11, 1933	Premieres Wallingford Riegger's *Divertissement* (Barrère-Salzedo-Britt, N.Y.)
Spring 1934	Named Chevalier de Légion d'Honneur by French government
July 23, 1935	Purchases Haynes platinum flute; first public performance, July 28
February 16, 1936	Premieres Edgard Varèse's *Density 21.5* (N.Y.)
April 10, 1937	Premieres Paul Hindemith's sonata (with Jesus M. Sanromá, Library of Congress)
1937	Forms Barrère-Britt Concertino, Barrère Trio
March 18, 1938	Premieres Bernard Wagenaar's *Triple Concerto* (Barrère-Salzedo-Britt, Philadelphia Orchestra/Ormandy, Philadelphia)
December 18, 1938	Premieres Philippe Gaubert's *Sonatine,* Marion Bauer's *Five Greek Lyrics,* Richard Franko Goldman's *Divertimento;* N.Y. premiere of Eugene Goossens's *Three Pictures* (with Richard Franko Goldman, Jerome Rappaport; New York Flute Club)
August 17, 1941	Last concert appearance, a broadcast performance of Mozart's *Concerto in G* with Chautauqua Symphony Orchestra/Stoessel
August 22, 1941	Suffers first stroke, Woodstock, N.Y.
June 14, 1944	Dies in Kingston, N.Y.

THE PUBLISHED MUSIC OF GEORGES BARRÈRE

PEDAGOGICAL LITERATURE

The flutist's formulae: A Compendium of Daily Studies on Six Basic Exercises. G. Schirmer, 1935.

Twenty-six studies from the method of Henry Altès. Edited by Georges Barrère. G. Schirmer, 1918.

Berbiguier, Benoit Tranquille. *Eighteen exercises or études for flute.* Revised and edited by Georges Barrère. G. Schirmer, 1918.

ORIGINAL COMPOSITIONS—FLUTE

Cadenzas for the Flute Concerto in D major (K. 314) by Mozart. Galaxy, 1939.

Cadenzas for the Flute Concerto in G major (K. 313) by Mozart. Galaxy, 1943.

Cadenzas for the Flute Concerto in G by Quantz. Edited by Frances Blaisdell. G. Schirmer, 1994.

ORIGINAL COMPOSITION—FLUTE AND PIANO

Nocturne. G. Schirmer, 1913.*

ORIGINAL COMPOSITION—THREE FLUTES

Deux pièces brèves pour trois flûtes. Carl Fischer, 1926.

ORIGINAL COMPOSITION—VOICE AND PIANO

Chanson d'automne (Song of autumn). Words by Paul Verlaine. English version by Henry Chapman. G. Schirmer, 1915.

TRANSCRIPTIONS AND ARRANGEMENTS, FLUTE AND PIANO

Aubert, Jacques. *Air.* G. Schirmer, 1928.*

Bach, J.S. *Arioso.* G. Schirmer, 1916.*

Bach, Johann Sebastian. *Badinerie from the Orchestral Suite in B minor.* Galaxy, 1941.

Bach, J.S. *Bourrée from the Overture or Orchestral Suite in B minor.* G. Schirmer, 1941.*

Bach, J.S. *Polonaise from the Orchestral Suite in B minor.* Galaxy, 1936.

Bach, J.S. *Siciliano.* G. Schirmer, 1922.*

Fauré, Gabriel. *Andantino.* G. Schirmer, 1929.*

Gluck, Christoph Willibald von. *Gavotte from the opera "Armide."* G. Schirmer, 1941.*

Gluck, Christoph Willibald von. *Scene from the opera "Orphéus."* G. Schirmer, 1923.*

Gluck, Christoph Willibald von. *Tambourin from the opera "Iphigénie en Aulide."* G. Schirmer, 1941.*

Grétry, André. *Passepied.* Galaxy, 1936.

Griffes, Chas. T. *Poem.* G. Schirmer, 1922.*

Leclair, Jean-Marie, l'aîné. *Gigue.* G. Schirmer, 1928.*

Leclair, Jean-Marie, l'aîné. *Musette.* G. Schirmer, 1925.*

Mondonville, Jean-Jacques C. de. *Tambourin.* G. Schirmer, 1929.*

Mozart, Wolfgang Amadeus. *Menuetto.* G. Schirmer, 1921.*

Rameau, Jean-Philippe. *Sarabande.* Galaxy, 1936.

Saint-Saëns, Camille. *Air de Ballet from "Ascanio."* Galaxy, 1936.

Saint-Saëns, Camille. *Le cygne (The swan).* G. Schirmer, 1930.*

Saint-Saëns, Camille. *Pavane.* G. Schirmer, 1928.*

Skilton, Charles Sanford. *Sioux Flute Serenade.* Carl Fischer, 1928.

Schumann, Robert. *The Prophet Bird, Op. 82, No. 7.* G. Schirmer, 1941.*

Tcherepnin, Nicolai. *Un air ancien (An Old Russian Melody).* G. Schirmer, 1935.*

Wormser, André. *Madrigal.* G. Schirmer, 1929.*

EDITIONS, FLUTE AND PIANO

Bach, J.S. *Sonatas for flute and piano.* Boston Music, 1944.

Handel, G.F. *Sonatas for flute and piano.* Boston Music, 1944.

ARRANGEMENTS, INDIVIDUAL WOODWINDS

Juilliard Intermediate Series of Solo Music of Wind Instruments. Selected & edited by Georges Barrère. Set One, works by Nicolai Tcherepnin in collaboration with Georges Barrère. *Un Air Ancien (Old Russian Melody),* flute and piano; *Pièce Calme (Pastorale),* oboe and piano; *Pièce insouciante (Carefree Tune),* clarinet and piano; *Variations simples,* bassoon and piano; *Fanfares,* trumpet/cornet and piano; *Une Oraison (Prayer),* bass trombone and piano. G. Schirmer, 1935.

ARRANGEMENTS, WOODWIND QUINTET

Juilliard Series of Music for Wind-Instruments. Twelve Transcriptions for Flute, Oboe, Clarinet, Bassoon and Horn. G. Schirmer, 1931.

Book I: Johann Sebastian Bach: *Sonatina, from the Cantata "Gottes Zeit ist die allerbeste Zeit" (Actus Tragicus)*; Harvey Worthington Loomis: *Around the Wigwam, Op. 76, No. 3*; Leo Delibes: *Petite Marche*; Franz Schubert: *Minuet, from Piano Sonata (Phantaisie) in G major, Op. 78*; Jean Philippe Rameau: *La Marais*; Katherine K. Davis: *Musette.*

Book II: Ludwig van Beethoven: *Adagio from the Sextet for Wind Instruments, Op. 71*; Roland Farley: *The Night Wind*; Edvard Hagerup Grieg: *Vöglein*; Wolfgang Amadeus Mozart: *Minuet*; Igor Stravinsky: *Pastorale*; David W. Guion: *The Harmonica-Player.*

Poldowski. *Suite Miniature for Wind Instruments.* Galamuse Instrumental Library No. 3. Galaxy, 1934.

*All pieces noted by an asterisk have been republished by G. Schirmer in *The Georges Barrère Album* (1994), with an introduction by Frances Blaisdell.

Address at the
Annual Dinner of the
New York Flute Club

March 25, 1923

Now that almost every large city in the U.S. has its Flute Club it will be interesting to decide what they are going to do with them.

What is a Flute Club?

I once heard this answer to the question. The first duty of a flute club is to fight for the CAUSE. How beautiful it sounds! Going back to the medieval times of the Crusades I can already imagine us, armed with our wood and silver Flutes going out in the world to fight the ENEMY. Alas! the trouble is just right here at the beginning: Who and Where is the ENEMY? You can scout as carefully as any Iroquois or Appalachian you will not discover this so much desired opponent. WHY? Because there is no one who has anything to say or to do against the flute and the flute players.

It is too easy for us to take the Quixotic attitude of nobody's victims and suffering of it. I certainly do not want to preach Couéism or any other optimistic form of belief or creed, but I am sure that everything is quite all right in the Flute World. In fact, I think that among the Wind Instruments Family, especially the Wood Winds, the Flute is rather privileged. Please realize that our instrument is the only one outside of the piano, violin, violoncello and harp that is programmed. Look on a full season's program of a large city's musical activities, and tell me how many oboists, clarinettists or bassoonists are featured. It is true that for one flute solo there are twenty-five for the violins, but this difference is even smaller than that existing between the other wood wind and the flute. So the situation is not as dark as the Crusaders would like to find it to have an excuse to throw their Boehm system weapons at the heads of the invaders, tyrants or enemies of any kind.

Since music is a civilized pastime, and even now that its mission seems somewhat changed, the flute has been favored by a special attention from the composers. To the few compositions for clarinet by the romantic Weber we can oppose the treasure of the sonatas by Johann Sebastien BACH and while we are not as fortunate as the same clarinet about Brahms we certainly stand first in the MOZART's bilan. Schumann has written few short pieces for the oboe but SCHUBERT's Variations for flute and piano are certainly tipping the scale. As for the Modern it will be too long to enumerate all of those who, though not being flute players themselves, have written for us. We can certainly exhibit a repertoire of uncomparable wealth starting with the mild REINECKE or the angelic

GODARD down to the subtle Griffes or the most aggressive KOECHLIN and Darius MILHAUD.

Truly, our colleagues who still confine themselves exclusively in the realm of the mediocre sentimentalism of a Terschak or the matter-of-fact of the Dopplers are hurting the famous CAUSE much more than the kind ultra-Modern Composer who pulls the Flute out of its supposed abandonment to deliver his revolutionary message through our medium. This is one more put over on the refloutable concurrence of the strings.

Why not decide that the real mission of a Flute Club is to promote better Music? Expose to the public our classical treasures, help the young composer and, above all, discard from our public repertoire these bookshelves mediocrities, reserving these relative masterworks for mere practice or historical study. Do not forget that pianists play Czerny every day in their Studios but never take him out. There is a reason and if we guess it we will accordingly treat our dear friends Walckiers, Boehm, Altès, Briccialdi with the same reserve that violinists treat Rode, Mazas, Ernst, Kreutzer, etc. We must not forget that even great Musicians very often misjudge new compositions at their first performance. Personally I remember having taken part in first productions of musical works supposed to be impossible to present, but which proved to be real popular successes in the course of time. You all know the tragedy of the fall of "Carmen" which caused the death of poor Bizet; and without looking so far back the divine "Afternoon of a Faune," delight of the Concert-goers of to-day was greeted by all kinds of cat calls when first played by the Colonne Orchestra in Paris less than thirty years ago.

While these views are purely personal I think they reflect quite closely the impression of the musical world at large. However, let us return to our dear little Flute Family.

At any rate, a flute club, like ours, shall always gather under the same banner of good friendship and sincere artistry, players of Demersseman and Kohler as well as essayists on Casella and Enesco, adepts of the Thumb Crutch together with the inexperienced antagonists of this addition to the flute anatomy; enemies of the open holes on the same level with French system's victims.

That is what a Flute Club is for: getting together good natured flutists of any standard. Unprejudiced amateurs, Artistic professionals all on perfect good terms with each other, regardless of school, system or aspiration. It is the chief aim of the New York Flute Club, I know, and it is to its prosperity that I raise my glass of iced water (awaiting for better times) as well as to the good health and long life of every one of its members and their families.

GEORGES BARRÈRE

Reprinted from The New York Flute Club souvenir booklet, May 1923.

SELECTED BIBLIOGRAPHY

Abbott, Lawrence F. "The Flute-Player." *Outlook,* 142 (17 February 1926), 243-244.

Allison, Lola. "George Barrère." *The Flutist,* 2, no. 2 (February 1921), 316-19; 2, no. 3 (March 1921), 340-42; 2, no. 4 (April 1921, 364-66. Reprinted in Leonardo De Lorenzo. *My Complete Story of the Flute.* Revised and Expanded Edition. Lubbock: Texas Tech University Press, 1992, pp. 182-97. [The earliest edition of Barrère's autobiography]

Barrère, Georges. *Georges Barrère.* New York: privately printed, [1928].

Barrère, Georges. "Expression Unconfined." *Musical Quarterly,* 30, no. 2 (April 1944), 192-97.

Barrère, Georges. "One in Two (Letter to my Cousins)." *Eolian Review,* 1, no. 2 (March 1922), 11-13.

Barrère, Georges. "Violin of the Wood Wind Instruments—the Flute." Translated by R. Champion. *Musical America,* November 6, 1909, p. 9.

Barrère, Georges. "What About the Flute?" An interview secured expressly for the *Étude Music Magazine* by R. H. Wollstein," *Étude,* 54, no. 6 (June 1936), 355-356.

Barrère, Georges. "Wood-Wind Instruments Attracting Women." *The Flutist,* 7, no. 12 (December 1926), 322.

Barrère, Georges. "The Woodwinds." In Robert E. Simon, Jr. *Be Your Own Music Critic: The Carnegie Hall Anniversary Lectures.* Garden City, N.Y.: Doubleday, Doran, 1941, pp. 215-41.

Blaisdell, Frances. "In Appreciation of Georges Barrère," *The Flutist Quarterly,* 12, no. 1 (Winter 1986), 41-46.

Damrosch, Walter. *My Musical Life.* New York: Charles Scribner's Sons, 1923.

Dorgeuille, Claude. *The French Flute School 1860-1950.* Translated and edited by Edward Blakeman. London: Tony Bingham, 1986.

Malkiel, Henrietta. "On Playing Minor Instruments. Georges Barrère, Flautist of the New York Symphony, Offers Suggestions for the Orchestral Rank and File." *The Musical Digest,* June 5, 1923, p. 15.

Martin, George. *The Damrosch Dynasty.* Boston: Houghton Mifflin, 1983.

Nelson, Susan. "Georges Barrère." *ARSC Journal,* 24, no. 1 (Spring 1993), 4-48. [Annotated discography]

The Platinum Flute and Georges Barrère. New York: [International Nickel Company], November 1935.

Sabin, Robert. "Georges Barrère Discusses Study of the Flute." *Musical America,* 48, no. 4 (25 October 1939), 31.

Toff, Nancy. *The Development of the Modern Flute.* Urbana: University of Illinois Press, 1986.

Wells, L. Jeanette. *A History of the Music Festival at Chautauqua Institution from 1874 to 1957.* Washington, D.C.: Catholic University of America Press, 1958.

ACKNOWLEDGMENTS

I would like to begin on a personal note and make special mention of two people who have provided me strong, direct links to Georges Barrère. Arthur Lora, his protégé, assistant, and eventual successor at Juilliard, was my major teacher. I regret deeply that he died just a few weeks after I began my research on Barrère, whom he so admired. However, his widow, Gloria Lora, and his daughter, Carina Irish, generously contributed recollections and vast amounts of memorabilia to this project. Arthur Lora passed along the spirit as well as the technique of the Barrère style in lessons punctuated by anecdotes of Barrère, the Maquarres, and other exemplars of the French flute-playing tradition, and in later years he enthusiastically encouraged me in my efforts to understand and to chronicle that tradition.

Most of all, I am grateful to Frances Blaisdell, whose idea it was to commemorate this diamond anniversary. Her vast store of knowledge about Barrère and about New York musical life over the past sixty-plus years has been an invaluable resource. She has tackled a continual stream of trivia questions, missing persons inquiries, and requests for photographs and documents with tireless energy and enthusiasm. But above all, she has been my loyal friend and advisor throughout the preparation of this exhibit, and I feel privileged to have enjoyed her collaboration.

This exhibit would not have been possible without the eager participation of the Barrère family, numerous students and colleagues of Barrère, and the devoted staffs of several libraries. Many of these people have consented to participate in an oral history project regarding Barrère and have graciously loaned valuable letters, photographs, programs, and other documents. Though not all of these items could be included in the exhibit, they have all been valuable assets to my research.

Donors to this exhibit are credited at the end of each catalog entry. The following abbreviations have been used:

LC: Music Division, Library of Congress
NYPL: Music Division, New York Public Library for the Performing Arts

I would particularly like to thank Jean Bowen, chief, Fran Barulich, and the entire staff of the music division, New York Public Library, who have assisted greatly in organizing this exhibit; Jane Gottlieb, head librarian, and Stephen Novak, archivist, The Juilliard School; Robert Sheldon, Wayne Shirley, William Parsons, Charles Sens, Kevin La Vine, and the staff of the Library of Congress Music Division; and Alfreda Locke Irwin, historian-in-residence, Chautauqua Historical Collection.

The following people have provided documents and photographs, taped interviews, done out-of-town research, provided leads to sources, and otherwise assisted my research: Donna K. Anderson, John Bailey, Julius Baker, Samuel Baron, Barbara (Mrs. Jean) Barrère, Hortense (Mrs. Gabriel) Barrère, Paul Barrère, Martin Bernstein, Frances Blaisdell, Herbert Blayman, Joyce Thompson Bottje, Bonita Boyd, Annabel Hulme Brieff, Frank Brieff, Lee Cioppa (admissions office, Manhattan School of Music), Nancy Clew, Mary C. (Mrs. Walter B.) Coleman, Samuel Coscia, Maxine Cutler, Julia Drumm Denecke, the late Lewis J. Deveau (Wm. S. Haynes Co.), Audrey DiChristina (assistant director of alumni affairs, The Juilliard School), Ruth Cubbage Dorsey, Charlotte Dykema, Paula Moskovitz Easton, Anita Haines Exline, Jill Felber, Harold Feldman, Francis E. Fitzgerald, Angeleita Floyd, Gino Franceschoni (archivist, Carnegie Hall), Ruth Freeman-Gudeman, Ray Friendly, John Fuggetta (Wm. S. Haynes Co.), Steve Gerber (Galaxy Publishing), Bernard Goldberg, Samuel Goldman, Nathan Gordon, Nathan Gottschalk, Genevieve Hall, Patricia Harper, Diana Haskell (Special Collections, The Newberry Library), Barbara Haws (archivist, New York Philharmonic), John Hein, Eric Hoover, James B. Hosmer, Carina Lora Irish, Sarah Jobin, Katherine Borst Jones, George Koutzen, Sherry and Walfrid Kujala, André Larson (curator, Shrine to Music Museum), Lucile Lawrence, Robert A. Lehman, Velma (Mrs. Donald) Lentz, Irving Levin, Herbert Levy, Bonnie Lichter, the late Gloria Lora, Edward Maisel, George W. Martin, Roger Mather, Stephen Maxym, Jean Klussman Morehead, Carolyn Grant Morey, George Morey, Susan Nelson, Lesley Greaves Oakes, Sandy Olson, Dewey Owens, Arthur Plettner, Gwen C. Powell, Bruce P. Price, J. Theodore Procházka (managing editor, Carl Fischer), Jerome Rappaport, René Rateau, Bill Rittman, Page Grosenbaugh Rowe, Gerald Rudy, Edith Sagul, Lois Schaefer, Sol Schoenbach, Morris Secon, Leonard Sharrow, Maxine L. Shimer, Nicolas Slonimsky, Christopher S. Smith, John H. Solum, Stephen Spackman, Robert Stuart, Parker Taylor, Jesse Teiko, W. Stephen Thomas, Everett and Jeanne Timm, Ira and Ruth Toff, Sidney (Mrs. Brian) Urquhart, Vincent Wagner (Music Director, The Maverick Concerts), Susan Waller, Judith Walsh (local history librarian, Brooklyn Public Library), David Walter, Jean Overman Whiton, Alexander Williams, Rosemary (Mrs. Meredith) Willson, Ransom Wilson, Larry Woodall, and Amy Zuback.

N.E.T.

INDEX